Simple Solutions.

Minutes a Day—Mastery for a Lifetime!

Common Core
ENGLISH GRAMMAR
& Mechanics

4

2nd Semester

Nancy L. McGraw
Nancy Tondy
Regina Webb

Joan Archer
Diane Dillon
Patricia Kecskemety

Bright Ideas Press, LLC
Cleveland, OH

Simple Solutions

Common Core
English Grammar & Mechanics 4
2nd Semester

Printed in the United States of America

The writers of *Simple Solutions* Common Core English Grammar & Mechanics aligned the series in accordance with information from the following:

National Governors Association Center for Best Practices,
Council of Chief State School Officers.
Common Core State Standards, English Language Arts.
National Governors Association Center for Best Practices,
Council of Chief State School Officers, Washington, D.C., 2010.

ISBN: 978-1-60873-230-2

Cover Design: Dan Mazzola
Editor: Rebecca Toukonen

Welcome

Simple Solutions.

Minutes a Day—Mastery for a Lifetime!

Name: _____

Room Number: _____

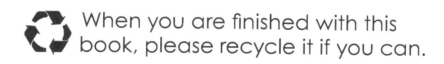

When you are finished with this book, please recycle it if you can.

Lesson #73

L.4.5c
1. Choose a word that means about the same as the underlined word.

The mother horse stayed close to its <u>foal</u>.

baby   horse   cowboy   trainer   calf

L.4.2d
2. Add -*ed* and -*ing* to these words.

cry   _____

_____

worry   _____

_____

study   _____

_____

L.4.1f
3. **A sentence is a group of words that expresses a complete thought. A sentence must include a subject and a verb.**

Circle the subject and underline the verb in the following sentences.

Galileo dropped objects from the Leaning Tower of Pisa.

He was observant.

L.4.4a
4. Choose the meaning of the underlined word.

Sheila stayed up too late last night, so she has felt <u>drowsy</u> all day.

sad   happy   worried   sleepy

L.4.2c
5. Add a comma to complete these compound sentences.

Example: Horace is fourteen now, so he can ride his bike to the park alone.

Shawn is finishing his homework but he is also listening to music.

He says he can do both yet his homework grades are dropping.

L.4.1d   6. **A noun may be described by more than one adjective. An adjective that tells age usually comes <u>before</u> an adjective that tells color.**

Underline the adjective that tells age and circle the adjective that tells color.

My old gray sweatshirt is torn in several places.

Don't forget to buy fresh green limes.

L.4.1b   7. Complete the sentence. Choose the future progressive form of the verb.

Next week, we _____ to the Cavs game.

will be going   went   were going

L.4.3c   8. Write F for formal English or I for informal English.

_____ Sir, may I help you?

_____ Yeah, that's it.

_____ Yes, you are correct.

L.4.1g   9. Choose the correct words to complete the sentence.

Please _____ a _____ of _____s for us to eat.

pear   pair   pare

L.4.2a   10. Rewrite any capitalization errors on the line.

i wrote a thank-you note to aunt bee for taking us to macy's, the big department store on ridge road.

_____

Lesson #74

W.4.5   1. Rewrite the sentence below with corrections.

Please tell <u>mariah</u> to ~~to~~ get her coat, hat.

                                                    ^and

_____

L.4.4b   2. Remember, a root word has no prefix or suffix.
What is the root of all of these words?   _____

     action   acted   inaction   acting

L.4.1c   3. The word *could* expresses less certainty than *can*.

     Example: I <u>can</u> speak Italian. (definitely)

                   I <u>could</u> go to Italy this summer. (maybe)

Choose the verb that expresses the right amount of certainty for each sentence.

Yes, I (could / can) read that sign from here.

Maybe Mary (could / can) go in my place.

L.4.5c   4. Choose the meaning of the underlined word.

     My baby brother lets out a <u>wail</u> when he feels hungry.

     giggle   large fish   loud cry   soft sound

L.4.2d   5. Write the plurals.

     patch   _____

     city   _____

     mouse   _____

L.4.1f   6. **A fragment is <u>not</u> a sentence because it does not express a complete thought.**

What is missing from this fragment?

   Twenty gray geese.

   subject   verb

Correctly rewrite it as a complete sentence.
(Hint: Include proper capitalization and punctuation.)

_____

_____

L.4.2a   7. Rewrite the sentence correcting all capitalization errors.

yesterday, mr. reynolds introduced reverend johnson to my grandfather.

_____

_____

L.3.1a   8. Underline the common nouns in this sentence.

Phyllis gave Terrence a book about rabbits and other animals of North America.

RF.4.3a 9. Choose the best word to complete the sentence.

The _____ section of the band includes the drums.

   percussion   obstacle   cooperate

L.4.2b   10. Add a comma and quotation marks.

Before you is the birthplace of Thomas Edison explained the tour guide.

Lesson #75

L.4.1c   1. *May* and *might* are helping verbs that express the possibility of the main verb.

     possibility   I *may* <u>become</u> a doctor.

     slight possibility   I *might* even <u>become</u> a surgeon.

Choose the verb that expresses possibility in the first sentence and the verb that expresses slight possibility in the second sentence.   (Hint: Use *might* for the slight possibility.)

After my last victory, I (may / might) make the ski team.

If I keep winning, I (may / might) even win an Olympic medal.

L.4.4a   2. Read the sentence.

My dog puts her toys behind the couch to <u>conceal</u> them.

What does *conceal* mean?

     drop   eat   hide   play

L.4.1b   3. Complete the sentence. Write the past progressive form of the verb *arrive*.

We _____ _____ for your birthday party.

L.4.1g   4. Choose the correct word.

The sun's (rays / raise) cause the sunflowers to (rays / raise) their heads.

The students became (board / bored) while the guest lecturer wrote on the (board / bored).

L.4.5a   5. Underline the simile in the following sentence.

Although Grandpa is 90, his mind is as sharp as a tack.

L.4.3   6. Complete the sentences with a word from the word box.

compound	simple	conjunction

A _____ sentence has one complete thought.

A _____ sentence has more than one complete thought.

L.3.1a   7. Underline the adverb. Draw an arrow to the verb it describes.

The class walked quietly.

L.4.1d   8. **A noun may be described by more than one adjective. An adjective that tells size usually comes <u>before</u> an adjective that tells age.** Underline the adjective that tells size and circle the adjective that tells age.

The big old dictionary lay unopened on the table.

The slender young plant would grow quickly in the sunshine.

L.4.1f   9. Read the fragment.

Is going to be ready on time.

What is missing from this fragment?   subject   verb

Correctly rewrite it as a complete sentence.

_____

_____

L.4.5c   10. Choose a synonym for the underlined word.

The <u>infant</u> was just learning to crawl.

sister   boy   baby   puppy

Lesson #76

L.4.1f   1. **A fragment is not a complete sentence.** Draw a line through the fragment.

It was getting late. The children in pajamas. Everyone was ready for a good bedtime story. Mother chose a favorite book from the shelf.

L.4.5a   2. Underline the simile in the following sentence.

Mom said my room was as dirty as a pigsty.

What is the meaning of the simile?
A) My room was messy.
B) A pig had been in my room.
C) My mom was cleaning.

L.4.1b   3. Complete the sentence. Write the future progressive form of the verb *pass*.

Jessica _____ _____ _____ out the papers for Mrs. Gruber.

L.4.1d   4. **A noun may be described by more than one adjective. An adjective that tells shape usually comes <u>before</u> an adjective that tells color.** Underline the adjective that tells shape and circle the adjective that tells color.

I rushed to open the rectangular pink envelope.

Mark used an oblong white towel to wipe up the milk.

L.4.4b   5. What is the root of these words?   _____

happily   happiness   unhappy   happier

W.4.5   6. Use the proofreader's symbol for "make capital" under the letters that should be capitalized. (See the *Help Pages*.)

yesterday, julia and i made brownies.

L.4.2c   7. Decide which of these is a compound sentence. Insert a comma.

It is starting to snow so we should wear our winter coats.

I'll bring my hat and mittens, too.

L.4.2a   8. Rewrite any capitalization errors on the line.

my sister is arriving from san antonio, texas for christmas.

_____

L.3.1a   9. Underline the singular possessive noun. Circle the plural possessive noun.

Jerri's favorite sport is women's basketball.

L.4.2d   10. **When a word ends in a consonant + *y* pattern, usually change the *y* to *i* when adding a suffix**.

Add –*ly* and –*ness* to these words.

happy   _____

        _____

sloppy   _____

        _____

Lesson #77

L.4.5b   1. **An idiom is a phrase whose meaning can't be understood from the individual words in it.**

Example: Of all the floats in the parade, this one takes the cake.

Takes the cake could mean someone is actually taking a cake. The idiom *takes the cake* means something is incredible or is more remarkable than something else.

An idiom is underlined below. What does the idiom mean?

"Our team won the championship, so let's <u>kick up our heels</u>."

A) put your heels in the air

B) go to the next game

C) celebrate

D) take off your shoes

L.4.4a   2. Read the sentence.

Germaine <u>doused</u> the campfire with water.

What is the meaning of the verb in the sentence above?

burned   soaked   cooked   none of these

L.4.3   3.   Which is a compound sentence?

_____ I don't have enough money for the movies today.

_____ Let's go for pizza today, and we can go to the movies on Friday.

L.4.5c   4. Which is a synonym for the underlined word?

The heavy sunflower is held up by a <u>rigid</u> stem.

stiff   colorful   easy   flexible

L.4.3c   5. Write F for formal English or I for informal English.

    _____ This video game is so cool.

    _____ Have you returned your library book?

L.3.1a   6. Underline the adverb that tells *when*.

    We sometimes celebrate Valentine's Day with a party.

L.4.1f   7. **A sentence tells a complete thought.**
Which of these is a sentence?
A) Barking all night.
B) Mom changed the light.
C) Fast red car.

L.4.1b   8. Complete the sentence. Write the present progressive form of the verb *attend*.

    She _____ _____ our school this year.

L.4.1g   9. Match the correct spelling of each word with its definition.

    _____ its   A) contraction of it is

    _____ it's   B) the possessive form of it

    _____ stare   C) (verb) to look intently

    _____ stair   D) (noun) a step going from one level to another

RF.4.3a   10. Choose the best word to complete the sentence.

    Our teacher assigned _____ problems for extra credit.

       essential   additional   protection

Lesson #78

L.4.4b   1. What is the root of these words? _____

      incorrect   correctly   corrected   incorrectly

L.4.2b   2. Add a comma and quotation marks.

      Uncle Jake recalled When I was your age, I walked 3 miles to school.

L.4.1c   3. Choose the verb that expresses *possibility* in the first sentence and the verb that expresses *slight possibility* in the second sentence.

      The theater said there (may / might) still be tickets.

      I heard the tickets (may / might) even be in the front row.

L.4.4b   4. Prefixes change the meaning of a root word. The prefix *un-* means "not." Add *un-* to make the opposite of the root word.

      clear   _____

      button   _____

L.4.2d   5. **In most cases, when adding a suffix that begins with a consonant, do not change the spelling of the base word.**

      Examples: joy + ful → joyful   pain + ful → painful
                  sincere + ly → sincerely

      Add the suffix *-ful* to these words.

      harm   _____

      play   _____

      cheer   _____

L.4.2c   6. Add a comma before the coordinating conjunction.

      I already have glue but I will need scissors to make the mask.

L.4.5a   7.   Underline the simile in the following sentence.

After a day of cleaning, our house was as clean as a whistle.

What is the meaning of the simile?

A) The house was clean, and a whistle needs to be clean in order to make noise.

B) We blew a whistle after we finished cleaning.

C) You must clean out the whistle before using it.

L.4.5b   8.   **An idiom has a special meaning in a certain language**. It is not a literal meaning. For example, in the United States we say "Don't beat around the bush!" This statement has nothing to do with *beating* or *bushes*. It means something like this: "Get to the point!"

What is the meaning of the underlined idiom?

You can get that floor clean with a little <u>elbow grease</u>.

_____ a type of cleaning solution

_____ hard work

_____ a tool for scrubbing

L.4.1f   9.   Draw a line through the fragment.

On quiet winter mornings, I see deer wandering in my backyard.

They are looking for water. Or maybe some food.

Rewrite the fragment as a complete thought.

_____

W.4.5   10.   Use the proofreader's symbol for "add something" to fix this sentence.

Althea Gibson was first African American to win the Female Athlete of the Year Award.

Lesson #79

L.4.1d   1.   **A noun may be described by more than one adjective. An adjective that states an opinion always comes <u>after</u> an adjective that tells number.** Underline the adjective that tells number and circle the adjective that states an opinion.

We gobbled down six fabulous brownies.

Henri bought a dozen inexpensive pencils.

L.4.1g   2.   Choose the correct word from the word box to complete the sentence.

two	too	to

Did you send letters _____ your grandparents, _____ ?

L.4.1b   3.   Complete the sentence. Choose the present progressive form of the verb.

My family _____ at the new resort.

stays   is staying   was staying

L.4.5c   4.   Choose the two antonyms.

_____ smile

_____ red

_____ scowl

_____ blue

L.3.1a   5.   Underline the nouns that are plural.

The rabbits ate carrots, radishes, and a head of lettuce.

L.4.1f   6.   Choose the group of words that is a sentence.

Can't find it.   The bearded man.   Let's get going.

L.4.1c   7. The helping verb *may* asks for permission.

Example: May I stay a little longer? Yes, you may.

Match each sentence with the way *may* is used.

_____   "possibility"   A) You may bring two friends.

_____   "permission"   B) I may eat lunch before I go.

L.4.3   8. What is the sentence type?

Where's Jimmy?

A) imperative

B) exclamatory

C) interrogative

D) declarative

L.4.4a   9. Read the sentence.

Tristan wasn't feeling well and had no <u>appetite</u> for supper.

What is the meaning of *appetite* in this sentence?

A) a feeling of enthusiasm

B) a distaste for beets

C) a need to cook

D) a desire for food

L.4.5b   10. Read the sentence and write the meaning of the underlined idiom in your own words.

The movers knew they were <u>in hot water</u> when Mom showed them the box of broken dishes.

_____

_____

Lesson #80

W.4.5   1. A proper noun always begins with a capital letter. Use a proofreader's symbol to correct this sentence. (See the *Help Pages*.)

Jenna and lisa have a lemonade stand.

L.4.5c   2. Are the underlined words synonyms or antonyms?

The choir's first performance was <u>dreadful</u>, but I found their last performance to be <u>exceptional</u>.

synonyms   antonyms

L.4.2d   3. Write the plural form of each word.

wolf   _____

trouble   _____

city   _____

RF.4.3a   4. Choose the best word to complete the sentence.

We stored all the baseball _____ in the gym.

equipment   compliment   progress

L.4.1f   5. Correctly rewrite this fragment as a sentence.

Are traveling by themselves to San Francisco.

_____

_____

L.3.1a   6. Underline the adverb. Draw an arrow to the verb it describes.

Dad snored noisily.

L.4.5a   7. Underline the two things being compared in the metaphor. Then write what the metaphor means on the line below.

Jonathon was a skyscraper in the room filled with babies and toddlers.

_____

L.4.3   8. A sentence always begins with a capital letter and ends with a punctuation mark. Underline the sentence that is correct.

We couldn't stop laughing!

Grandma is coming for dinner

did Max leave his video game here?

L.4.2a   9. Rewrite any capitalization errors on the line.

steamboat and snowmass are two ski resorts on the eastern peaks of the rocky mountains.

_____

L.4.4b   10. Three more prefixes that mean "not" are *in-*, *ir-*, and *dis-*.

Match each word with its meaning.

_____ invalid   A) not responsible

_____ irresponsible   B) not showing respect

_____ disrespect   C) not valid

Lesson #81

L.4.3   1. Make a compound sentence from the two simple sentences.

I don't know how to cook. I am going to take lessons.

_____

_____

_____

L.4.1f   2. A sentence tells a complete thought. Choose
             the group of words that is a sentence.
             A) Frank won again!
             B) Thirty sharp pencils.
             C) Asked for seconds.

L.4.4c   3. Use a dictionary to find the meaning
             of each word. Choose the correct word,
             then identify its part of speech.

I (new / knew) you would like this.   _____

I put a bandage on the blister on
my (heal / heel).   _____

L.4.4a   4. Read the sentence.

Your little dog follows you everywhere. He is so <u>devoted</u> to you!

What does the underlined word mean?

loyal   afraid   sleepy   smart

L.4.2c   5. Place a comma in the following sentence.

Ketzia was late for school but she did not receive a detention.

L.4.5c   6. Write a word that ends in *–ment* and is a synonym for *quarrel*.

The boys had an _____ about who would be first.

L.4.1d   7. Complete the sentence by writing the adjectives in the correct order. See the *Help Pages* if you are not sure which adjective should come first.

oval   beautiful

He photographed Angelica's _____ _____ face.

L.4.3c   8. Write F for formal English or I for informal English.

_____ Sara, please set the table.

_____ When are we gonna chow down?

_____ Please place your napkin on your lap.

_____ These burgers are super awesome!

L.4.1b   9. Complete the sentence. Choose the future progressive form of the verb.

She _____ _____ _____ at her favorite restaurant.

     is eating   will be eating   eats

L.4.2b   10. Add a comma and quotation marks.

We will come back next year and stay

for two weeks vowed Grandpa.

Lesson #82

L.4.2d   1. Check the spelling of these plurals. Cross out any misspelled words.

      sheeps   boxs   trees   childs   wolves   clutches

      Write the misspelled words correctly.

_____

L.4.1f   2. Draw a line through the fragment.

      People light candles to celebrate all the December holidays. Christmas, Hanukkah, and Kwanzaa. They use candles as symbols of light, life, and hope.

      Rewrite the fragment as a complete thought.

_____

_____

L.4.4c   3. Find the word *prominent* in the dictionary and read its definition. Choose the sentence in which *prominent* is used correctly.

      A) Benjamin Franklin was a prominent citizen in his time.

      B) I can never find my keys because they are always in a prominent place.

L.4.1d   4. Complete the sentence by writing the adjectives in the correct order. See the *Help Pages* if you are not sure which adjective should come first.

red   antique

      There was a(n) _____ _____ fire engine in the parade.

L.3.1a   5. Choose a present tense verb.

      Mona and Tierra (play / plays) the harp.

L.4.5b   6. What does the idiom mean?

Many homes were damaged in the tornado. Everyone who can is donating food and clothing or <u>lending a hand</u>.

_____

L.4.2c   7. Decide which of these is a compound sentence. Insert a comma.

Carla thinks she saw that movie but she can't remember the plot.

It starred a magician who did card tricks and tricks of illusion.

L.4.5a   8. Underline the simile in the following sentence.

Since he's been working out, my brother is as strong as an ox.

What is the meaning of the simile?
A) My brother likes to exercise.
B) My brother has strong muscles.
C) My brother looks like an ox.

L.4.1b   9. Complete the sentence. Choose the present progressive form of the verb.

Mom _____ us to soccer practice.

   will be driving   is driving   drives

L.4.4a 10. Read the sentence.

Spending more than you can afford for a coat is an <u>imprudent</u> purchase.

Which word means about the same as _imprudent_?

   unkind   fluffy   warm   foolhardy

Lesson #83

L.4.5c   1. Choose a synonym for the underlined word.

The goslings followed the mother goose.

baby geese   hunters   insects   children

L.4.1d   2. Complete the sentence by writing the adjectives in the correct order.

blue   square

The _____ _____ book had not been borrowed in years.

W.4.5   3. Use three proofreader's symbols to correct the sentence below.

In 1984, Oprah Winfrey she became the fist African American woman to co-anchor the news in Nashville, Tennessee

L.4.3   4. **A compound sentence has more than one complete thought. It uses a coordinating conjunction to connect parts of sentences to each other**.

Which is a compound sentence?

_____ The car slid on the ice, and it rolled into the ditch.

_____ A tow truck came to pull it out.

L.4.3c   5. Write F for formal English or I for informal English.

_____ I like to listen to this song.

_____ This music rocks!

L.4.2b   6. Add a comma and quotation marks.

Aiden chuckled I did not recognize you in that cow costume!

L.4.1c   7. **The helping verb *should* plus a main verb suggests "probably" or "supposed to."**

supposed to   You should do your best work.

probably   The letter should arrive today.

_____ supposed to   A) The passengers should be boarding soon.

_____ probably   B) The dentist said we should floss after eating.

L.4.4b   8. Suffixes are word endings that change the meaning of a word. Match these suffixes with their meanings.

_____ -er   A) without

_____ -est   B) more

_____ -ful   C) full of

_____ -less   D) most

L.4.1f   9. Choose the group of words that is a sentence.

A) Empty cardboard box.

B) Stuck in the ditch.

C) Melinda coasted to the finish.

L.4.4c   10. Find the word *brooch* in the dictionary. Look at the pronunciation and meaning of brooch. What is a *brooch*?

a bridge   a group of animals   a pin   none of these

Does brooch rhyme with *coach* or *much*? _____

Lesson #84

L.4.2c   1. Place commas as needed in any compound sentences.

      We finished our snowman and we went inside for hot cocoa.

      We enjoyed the cocoa but we couldn't wait to go back out.

      We decided to build a snow fort and another snowman.

L.4.5a   2. Underline the two things being compared in the metaphor. Then write what the metaphor means on the line below.

      Jeremiah was a turtle getting ready for school each morning.

      _____

L.4.1g   3. Choose the correct word.

      It is no small (feat / feet) to walk on your hands with your (feat / feet) in the air.

      I will be the (loan / lone) person in the class without a pencil unless someone has one to (loan / lone) me.

L.4.1b   4. Complete the sentence. Choose the past progressive form of the verb.

      Jonah _____ on the trampoline in my yard.

        will be jumping   is jumping   was jumping

L.4.4a   5. Read the sentence.

      Nathan finished his homework <u>just</u> before dinner.

      What does the underlined word mean?

       fair   simply   shortly   wrong

L.4.2a   6. **When you write the title of a magazine, capitalize the first, last, and most important words in the title**.

Write the magazine titles correctly.

My dad subscribes to *vegetarian times*, and my mom subscribes to *women's health and fitness*.

_____

_____

L.4.5c   7. Which two words are synonyms?

impatient   unmovable   immobile   uncomfortable

L.4.5b   8. Tell the meaning of this idiom in your own words.

I'm sure I got a good grade. That quiz was a <u>piece of cake</u>.

_____

L.3.1a   9. Underline the adverb. Draw an arrow to the verb it describes.

Write your name neatly.

L.4.1f   10. A fragment is not a complete thought. Draw a line through the fragment.

The Hopewell Indians were Mound Builders. Many beautiful artifacts. These artifacts teach us about the lifestyle of the Hopewell.

Rewrite the fragment as a complete thought.

_____

_____

Lesson #85

L.4.2b   1. Add a comma and quotation marks.

Susie challenged How about a
rematch of our ping pong game?

L.4.1f   2. Draw a line through the fragment.

There were rakes, picks, and brooms everywhere. But no shovel.

Finally, they decided to borrow one from their neighbor.

Rewrite the fragment as a complete thought.

_____

L.4.1a   3. **The relative pronouns are *who, whose, whom, which*, and *that*.**
Relative pronouns introduce a part of a sentence that is related or
connected to an antecedent.

antecedent   relative pronoun (relates to students)
↓   ↓
Example: The students who play tennis will leave at noon.
describes students

Underline the relative pronoun. Draw an arrow to the antecedent.

The actors who are in the play may leave at 2 p.m.

L.4.4b   4. Words that have *pedi-* or *ped-* are from a Latin word that means "foot."
See if you can match these words with their meanings.

_____   pedicure   A) a treatment for the feet

_____   pedestrian   B) a person walking

L.4.1c   5. Write a sentence. Use *should* plus a main verb.

_____

_____

L.4.4c   6. Check the spelling of these words with a dictionary. Cross out any misspelled words and rewrite them.

usually   adoreable   coarse   wether

_____

L.4.1d   7. Complete the sentence by writing the adjectives in the correct order.

| oval   multicolored |

Shelley hid the _____

_____ shapes in the grass

for the egg hunt.

L.3.1a   8. Underline the proper nouns.

"If you finish all your vegetables, there are Klondike Bars and Snickers Bars in the freezer," said Grandma.

RF.4.3a   9. Choose the best word to complete the sentence.

Cliff was the most talented _____ in the band.

A) musician

B) alphabetical

C) precipitation

W.4.5   10. Use proofreader's symbols to show which letters should be capitalized.

you and i are in the same class.

Rewrite the sentence you edited.

_____

Lesson #86

L.4.1g   1. Choose the correct word.

The (night / knight) drew his sword and prepared to do battle.

L.4.3   2. Combine these two sentences to make a compound sentence. (Hint: The sentence will have two complete thoughts joined by a coordinating conjunction.)

June plays soccer. June enjoys watching movies.

_____

_____

L.4.1b   3. Complete the sentence. Write the present progressive form of the verb *search*.

My dog, Brady, _____ for his toy.

L.4.2c   4. Place a check next to the sentence that has two complete thoughts linked by a coordinating conjunction. Add a comma.

_____ The Cumberland Gap is beautiful and enjoyable to hike.

_____ Luckily I brought my hiking boots and I can probably find a good hiking stick.

L.4.2d   5. Correctly spell the plurals of these words. The first one has been done for you.

baby _____ babies _____

daisy _____

penny _____

city _____

L.4.5c   6. Use the prefix *dis-* to write an antonym
for *infected*.

_____

L.4.1f   7. Correctly rewrite this fragment as a sentence.

The best thing about September.

_____

L.4.4a   8. Look at the underlined words and match each word with its meaning.

The <u>authorship</u> of that <u>ancient</u> work is <u>anonymous</u>.
         A   B   C

_____ an unknown person

_____ very old

_____ creator / origin of written work

L.4.1a   9. **The relative pronouns are *who, whose, whom, which,* and *that*.**
Relative pronouns are related, or connected, to an antecedent.

                   antecedent   relative pronoun (refers to puppies)
                       ↓   ↓

Example: The puppies <u>that</u> were born in
              March are ready for adoption.

Underline the relative pronoun.
Draw an arrow to the antecedent

The girls who ate the pizza got sick.

L.4.5a   10. Underline the simile in the following sentence.

Attending the concert was like listening to a choir of angels.

What is the meaning of the simile?
A) Angels were singing.
B) The singing at the concert was beautiful.
C) The concert was cancelled.

Lesson #87

L.4.1a 1. **The relative pronouns are *who, whose, whom, which,* and *that*.**
Relative pronouns are related, or connected, to an antecedent.

Underline the relative pronoun. Draw an arrow to the antecedent.

The leaders who wanted to write new laws met last week.

L.4.1f 2. What is missing from this fragment?   subject   verb

Is disappointed because of the weather.

Correctly rewrite it as a complete sentence.

_____

L.4.4c 3. Use the dictionary to check the spelling of these words. Cross out any misspelled words and rewrite them.

travel   languege   figgur   interest

_____

L.4.1g 4. Match the correct spelling of each word with its definition.

_____ seem   A) a noun referring to the place where two pieces of cloth are sewn together

_____ seam   B) a verb meaning to appear to be something or do something

_____ horse   C) (noun) a four-legged animal

_____ hoarse   D) (adjective) describes a rough or harsh voice

W.4.5 5. Use proofreader's symbols to make two corrections.

no, sarah, don't go near the fire!

L.4.3   6. Underline the complete predicate in this sentence.

The classes went to the cafeteria for the Kwanzaa festival.

L.4.4b   7. The prefixes that mean "not" are *un-*, *im-*, *il-*, *dis-*, *in-*, and *ir-*.
Use these prefixes to make words mean the opposite of their roots.
Example: in + correct → incorrect (not correct)

Use *il-* to write a word that means the
opposite of *legible*.   _____

L.4.1d   8. Complete the sentence by writing the adjectives in the correct order.

dozen	tiny

Sylvia carefully placed a _____ _____ stars
on each invitation.

L.4.3c   9. Write F for formal English or I for informal English.

_____ Hey, let's go now!

_____ Would you like coffee or tea?

_____ Thank you for your help.

_____ Those are some cool shoes.

L.4.4a   10. Read the sentence.

The <u>shallow</u> water barely covered my ankles.

What does *shallow* mean?

deep   muddy   low   cold

Lesson #88

L.4.5b   1. Underline the figure of speech. Explain what it means on the line below.

Your goose is cooked if you don't keep your promise.

_____

L.4.1c   2. **Will is a helping verb that expresses readiness to do something. Would is used when there is a condition that prevents the action from happening. Would is also used with a main verb to be polite.**
Examples:

I *will* go to the party.	Action is going to happen.
I *would* bake rolls, but I'm out of flour.	A condition prevents the action from happening.
I *would* like an extra blanket.	polite

Match each sentence to the way *will* and *would* are being used in the sentence.

_____ Action is going to happen.

_____ A condition prevents action from happening.

_____ polite

A) I would like some more tea.

B) Lance would ride his bike to school if it would stop raining.

C) I will have money left over.

L.4.1a   3. *Who, whose,* and *whom* refer to people. Underline the relative pronoun. Draw an arrow to the antecedent.

The photographer whose pictures are on display is here!

L.4.5c   4. Read the sentence.

Janice shouted with <u>glee</u> when she saw all the gifts.

Choose a synonym for the underlined word.

fear   anger   loud   joy

L.4.5b   5. What does the underlined idiom mean?

Linda studied for the test, but she only passed <u>by the skin of her teeth</u>.

_____

_____

L.4.2d   6. Choose the correct spelling of a word that means "every year."

yeary   yealy   yerly   yearly

L.4.2c   7. Add a comma before the coordinating conjunction.

Are you ready to order or do you need a few more minutes?

L.4.2b   8. Add a comma and quotation marks.

Jackie gushed These are the prettiest holiday lights I have ever seen!

L.4.1f   9. Remember, **a sentence is a group of words that is a complete thought**. Underline the group of words that is a fragment.

We visited the Grand Canyon. Stayed in a tent.

L.4.1b   10. Complete the sentence. Write the future progressive form of the verb *help*.

Our friends _____ to plan the surprise party.

Lesson #89

L.4.4a   1. Choose the meaning of the underlined word.

Patty was sick all weekend, and she is still feeling a little <u>feeble</u>.

     better   weak   strong   tough

L.4.1e   2. **A preposition shows how words in a sentence are related. A noun or a pronoun comes after a preposition.** Use the *Help Pages* to write five prepositions below.

_____

L.4.5c   3. Choose a synonym for the underlined word.

KaMicha knows how to <u>mend</u> a torn net.
A) broken
B) woven
C) repair
D) replace

L.4.1d   4. Complete the sentence by writing the adjectives in the correct order.

purple   scariest

Justin wore the _____ _____ mask I'd ever seen.

L.4.1a   5. Choose the correct relative pronoun. The antecedent can be a noun or pronoun.

The person _____ keys you need has already left.

     whose   that   who

L.4.2a   6. Write these names correctly.

mrs. whitman   senator brown

_____

L.4.4b　7. Words containing the root *graph* come from a Greek word that means "write." Use what you know about other origins to match these words with their meanings.

_____ autograph　　A) a section of writing

_____ graphite　　B) written in one's own hand

_____ paragraph　　C) material used for writing

L.4.1f　8. Draw a line through the fragment.

Jane and Zani visited me at my house last night. We ate pizza, watched TV, and played board games. They left this morning. Didn't know what to do. I decided to take a walk, and you'll never believe what I saw.

L.4.4c　9. Find the word *queue* in a dictionary and look at the pronunciation key. Which of these does the word *queue* sound like?

K　　Q　　C　　none of these

What is the meaning of *queue*?

_____ a row or line-up

_____ a type of fish

_____ a place in Canada

_____ none of these

L.4.3　10. Which is a compound sentence?

_____ Tom invited the new student to the picnic.

_____ Mario couldn't go, but he promised to go to the movies later.

Lesson #90

L.4.1f   1. Draw a line through the fragment.

Their mom asked them to do some gardening. They all put on gloves. And old clothes. She gave them each a trowel and some seeds.

L.4.5b   2. **An adage or proverb is a wise saying that most people think is true.**

Example: Don't count your chickens before they hatch.

The saying reminds us not to rely on something before it happens.

An adage is written below. What does it mean?

All that glitters is not gold.

A) Diamonds also glitter.

B) Just because something looks valuable doesn't mean it is valuable.

C) Gold is a soft metal.

RF.4.3a   3. Choose the best word to complete the sentence.

Mr. Bender gave us a _____ about our behavior.

equipment   compliment   progress

L.4.1e   4. **A preposition is a word that ties a noun or pronoun to other words in a sentence.** Some common prepositions are listed in the *Help Pages* in the back of this book. Find the list and write three prepositions here.

_____

L.4.2b   5. Add quotation marks.

Would you care for an ice cream sundae? offered the server.

L.4.1b 6. Complete the sentence. Choose the future progressive form of the verb.

I _____ to my new friends soon.

will be talking   talk   am talking

W.4.5 7. Use the proofreader's symbols for "make capital" and "check spelling" to correct this sentence.

The red fox lifes in almost all parts of North america.

L.4.1a 8. Complete the sentence.

Have you written to someone _____ lives in another country?

A) which

B) whose

C) who

L.4.5a 9. Underline the simile in the following sentence.

Liza is as happy as a clam when she has a new book and all evening to read.

What is the meaning of the simile?

A) Having a new book makes Liza content.

B) Liza likes clams.

C) Liza feels clammy when she's reading.

L.4.2c 10. Place a comma in the following sentence.

It is early in December but the ground is covered in snow!

Lesson #91

L.4.1d   1. Complete the sentence by writing the adjectives in the correct order.

younger   handsome

Have you noticed that Alexandra's _____

_____ brother looks just like her?

L.4.4c   2. Find the definition and pronunciation of the word *chalice* in a dictionary. What is a *chalice*?

small house   gold chain   metal cup   none of these

Which name rhymes with *chalice*?   Alice   Lisa   Blake

L.4.4b   3. Some other prefixes that mean "not" are *im-* and *il-*. For example, *illegal* means "not legal" and *impossible* means "not possible." Use these prefixes to reverse the meanings of these root words.

im + polite → _____

il + logical → _____

L.4.1e   4. **A preposition shows the relationship between words in a sentence.**

Example: Timmy hiked <u>through</u> the Grand Canyon.

Underline the preposition.

He walked beside his sister.

L.4.4a   5. If *uni-* means "one" and *bi-* means "two," why would it be more difficult to balance yourself on a unicycle than on a bicycle?

A unicycle _____.

is bigger   has one wheel   has two pedals

L.3.1a   6. Choose the correct spelling of the adverb.

Orville (careful / carefully) built wings for the machine.

L.4.1a   7. **_That_ is a relative pronoun used to refer to _things_** but may refer to people. Underline the relative pronoun. Draw an arrow to the antecedent.

Animals that sleep during the day and hunt at night are nocturnal.

L.4.3c   8. Write F for formal English or I for informal English.

_____ Wow, Krista! You aced your math test!

_____ I am pleased you did so well on your math test, Krista.

L.4.1f   9. **A run-on sentence improperly combines two or more sentences together as one sentence. A run-on sentence can be rewritten as two or more sentences.**

Look at this run-on sentence. Draw a line to show where one sentence should end and another should begin.

One rainy afternoon the children grew bored with television they started to look through the cupboards for board games to play.

L.4.1c   10. **_Ought_ is a helping verb and is used with a main verb in the same way as _should_.** While _should_ suggests ideal or probable situations, _ought_ is more insistent.

Examples: You _ought_ to <u>know</u> better.
                My niece _ought_ to <u>pay</u> the bill.

Choose between the verb that suggests the ideal situation and the verb that insists on the ideal situation.

We (should / ought to) call to see what the weather is like.

You (should / ought to) make sure the fire is completely out.

Lesson #92

L.4.2c   1. Add the comma to the compound sentence.

     A) Chuck Yeager was the first pilot to fly faster than the speed of sound.

     B) Many credit the Wright brothers with the first successful flight but others believe they were not the first.

     C) Amelia Earhart was the famous aviation pioneer who made a solo flight across the Atlantic Ocean.

L.4.1a   2. Choose the correct relative pronoun. The antecedent can be a noun or pronoun.

     A fact is a statement _____ you can prove.

        whom   that   who

L.4.1b   3. Complete the sentence. Choose the present progressive form of the verb.

     I _____ about signing up for piano lessons.

        will be thinking   think   am thinking

L.4.4c   4. Are you more *gregarious* or more *taciturn*? Choose the word you think best describes you and then look up the word in a dictionary. Write the meaning of the word you chose.

     gregarious   _____

     taciturn   _____

W.4.5   5. Which proper nouns need to be capitalized? Use the proofreader's symbol for "make capital."

     Julie and greg gave steven the book <u>Artemis Fowl</u>, written by eoin colfer.

L.4.1c   6. Write a sentence using the verb *would* as a polite expression with a main verb.

     _____

L.4.5a 7. Underline the simile in the following sentence.

When Brian found his car, the tire was as flat as a pancake.

What is the meaning of the simile?

A) Brian had pancakes for breakfast.

B) Brian's car had a flat tire.

C) Brian changed his tire.

L.4.5b 8. Read the sentence.

Shelley always <u>gets cold feet</u> right before a piano solo.

What does the idiom mean?

A) needs warmer socks

B) uses the foot pedals

C) becomes fearful or nervous

D) is cold

L.4.1f 9. Rewrite this run-on. Add capitalization and end punctuation.

Being fit and healthy means eating foods that are good for you get plenty of rest and activity every day, too.

_____

_____

_____

L.4.1e 10. Circle the preposition in each sentence. Use the *Help Pages* if needed.

Ryan looked through the catalog.

Rocky sat beside his brother.

Lesson #93

RF.4.3a   1. Choose the best word to complete the sentence.

Asking you to work quietly is a _____ request.

available   explosion   reasonable

L.4.2a   2. Place a check in front of the sentence that has correct capitalization. Correctly rewrite all words with capitalization errors.

_____ we are driving to greenwich village on the west side of manhattan.

_____ This Tuesday I am getting a new Trek, a bicycle manufactured in Waterloo, Wisconsin.

_____

RI.4.7   3 – 5. **Graphs, charts, tables, and diagrams show information graphically. You can understand and use the data quickly if you know how to read these visual displays.**

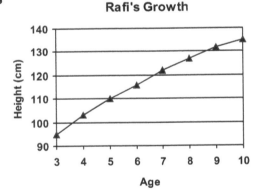

Rafi's Growth

Rafi's parents kept a record of his growth by measuring Rafi's height in centimeters. Here is a line graph showing Rafi's growth. A line graph shows changes over time.

What is the title of the graph? _____

How old was Rafi when his parents started to record his height? _____

Why does the line graph climb higher and farther to the right?

Rafi is getting older.   Rafi is getting taller.   Both are true.

If the trend continues, about how tall will Rafi be next year?

160 cm   125 cm   140 cm

L.4.3c   6. Write F for formal English or I for informal English.

_____ It's, like, so funny.

_____ The joke made us laugh.

L.4.4a   7. Read the sentence.

If you lose the game, don't <u>sulk</u>. You can try again next time.

If someone is *sulking*, what are they doing?

moping   feeling better   trying hard   winning

L.4.1f   8. Rewrite this run-on as two complete sentences.

If you like to write letters you may want to have a pen pal you can write to someone who lives very far away.

_____

_____

_____

L.4.5b   9. Match each idiom with its meaning.

_____ take on too big of a task   A) add fuel to the fire

_____ make matters worse   B) dry run

_____ rehearsal   C) bite off more than you can chew

L.4.1a   10. Choose the correct relative pronoun. The antecedent can be a noun or pronoun.

Children _____ parents are good cooks are very lucky!

that   whose   who

Lesson #94

L.4.1f   1. Rewrite this run-on.

The biggest snow storm of the year came on my birthday no one could go out I had to postpone my party!

_____

_____

_____

L.4.1b   2. Complete the sentence. Write the present progressive form of the verb *buy*.

Mrs. O'Hara _____ pizza for our class.

L.4.2c   3. Add a comma in the following sentence.

My cousin is coming to visit and she is bringing her skateboard.

L.4.5a   4. Underline the simile in the following sentence.

Julia forgot her sunscreen and now she is as red as a lobster.

What is the meaning of the simile?

A) Julia's sunscreen turned her skin red.

B) Julia got sunburned.

C) Julia loves lobster.

L.4.2a   5. Rewrite any capitalization errors on the line.

the smith family watched the movies *the croods* and *monsters university* while they were snowed in last january.

_____

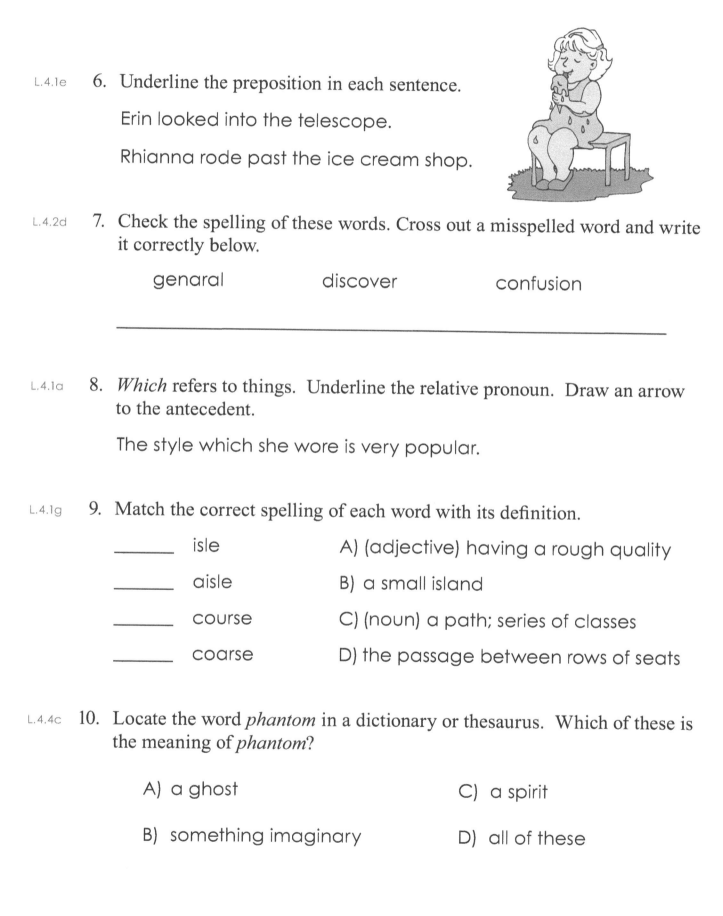

L.4.1e　6. Underline the preposition in each sentence.

Erin looked into the telescope.

Rhianna rode past the ice cream shop.

L.4.2d　7. Check the spelling of these words. Cross out a misspelled word and write it correctly below.

　　　　genaral　　　　discover　　　　confusion

　　　　_____

L.4.1a　8. *Which* refers to things. Underline the relative pronoun. Draw an arrow to the antecedent.

The style which she wore is very popular.

L.4.1g　9. Match the correct spelling of each word with its definition.

_____ isle　　　　A) (adjective) having a rough quality

_____ aisle　　　　B) a small island

_____ course　　　C) (noun) a path; series of classes

_____ coarse　　　D) the passage between rows of seats

L.4.4c　10. Locate the word *phantom* in a dictionary or thesaurus. Which of these is the meaning of *phantom*?

A) a ghost　　　　　　C) a spirit

B) something imaginary　　D) all of these

Lesson #95

L.4.5b   1. Read the sentences.

Deidre is organizing a surprise party for Paula. "Here she comes," Deidre said. "Mum's the word!"

What is the meaning of the idiom?

A) Put some mums in a vase.

B) Share the information.

C) Keep quiet, say nothing.

L.4.1f   2. Read this sentence carefully.

Phillis Wheatley was a gifted child who had been kidnapped from Africa and sold into slavery she learned to speak English and became an excellent poet but sadly she died young.

What is this?   fragment   run-on sentence

L.4.4a   3. Read the sentence.

Children <u>yearn</u> for summer vacation in the springtime.

What does *yearn* mean?

despise   long for   forget   climb

L.4.4b   4. Words that contain *auto* come from a Greek word that means "self." Use what you know to match these words with their meanings.

_____ autobiography   A) self-starting

_____ autograph   B) written by oneself

_____ automatic   C) the written story of one's own life

RF.4.3a   5. Choose the best word to complete the sentence.

Lines which intersect to form right angles are called _____ lines.

immediate   distinguish   perpendicular

L.4.1a   6. *Which* refers to things. Underline the relative pronoun. Draw an arrow to the antecedent.

Kate used a small notebook, which was perfect.

W.4.5   7. Look at the proofreader's symbols. Write this sentence correctly.

The red ~~gray~~ fox eats fruits and vegetables as well as small animals ⊙

_____

_____

L.4.1c   8. Choose between the verb that suggests the ideal situation and the verb that insists on the ideal situation.

Mindy (should / ought to) stay at home until she is not contagious.

You (should / ought to) come with us to the park.

L.4.1e   9. Underline the preposition in each sentence.

Abigail placed the cake on the table.

Dakota stored his supplies in his locker.

L.4.1d   10. Underline the adjectives that state an opinion.

The silly clowns juggled colorful balls while riding unicycles in the festive parade.

An annoying poodle yapped at their wheels.

Lesson #96

L.4.1e   1. List three more prepositions from the *Help Pages.* Do not repeat any prepositions that you already listed in previous lessons.

_____

L.4.1a   2. Choose the correct relative pronoun. The antecedent can be a noun or pronoun.

Bring the broom _____ is in the kitchen closet.

that   whose   whom

L.4.5a   3. Underline the simile in the following sentence.

The ocean waves looked like whipped cream on a caramel beach.

What is the meaning of the simile?

A) The waves looked white and fluffy.

B) There was ice cream on the beach.

C) You could eat the waves.

L.4.2d   4. Write the misspelled word correctly.

The coyote is a beautyful animal with striking yellow eyes, a bushy tail, and pointed ears.   _____

L.4.1f   5. Underline the sentence that has no errors.

We walked up and down the streets, searching for that dog. In people's back yards!

What is wrong with the other sentence?

_____

L.4.1g   6. Choose the correct word.

Turn (write / right) at the corner to find the bakery.

L.4.2c   7. Rewrite the sentence adding a comma and a conjunction.

No one came to the door I walked away from the house.

_____

_____

L.4.4c   8. Use a dictionary to find the word *impossible*. Write the word *impossible* in four syllables.

_____   _____   _____   _____

L.4.1b   9. Complete the sentence. Choose the past progressive form of the verb.

That restaurant _____ an "all you can eat" pancake breakfast.

    serves   was serving   is serving

L.4.5b   10. **An adage, or proverb, is a wise saying that most people think is true.** "The grass is always greener on the other side of the fence" is a proverb. The saying tells us that other people's things or situations often seem better than ours.

"A man is known by the company he keeps." This proverb means if you hang around with a liar or a thief, you may be thought of as a liar or a thief.

This saying advises a person to _____.

A) associate with kind, honest people

B) tattle on your friends

C) become a liar or a thief

Lesson #97

L.4.4a   1.   Read the sentence.

      Timothy is such a joker. He's always playing <u>pranks</u>.

      What are *pranks*?

        music   tricks   cards   sports

L.4.2d   2.   Sometimes the spelling of the root word changes when you add *-ion*, *-sion*, or *-tion*.

      Example: locate + ion → location

                   divide + sion → division

      Form the new words. Use a dictionary to check your work.

      create + ion →   _____

      decide + sion →   _____

L.3.1a   3.   **A possessive pronoun shows ownership. It takes the place of a possessive noun. Possessive pronouns may appear before a noun. The singular possessive pronouns are *my, your, her, his, its*. The plural possessive pronouns are *our, your, their*.**

      Use a possessive pronoun to replace the underlined word(s) in each sentence. One has been done for you.

      <u>Reese</u> zipped up <u>Reese's</u> coat.   _____her_____

      <u>Daniel</u> waited for <u>Daniel's</u> ride to come.   _____

      It's time for the students to turn in
 <u>the students</u>' gym uniforms.   _____

L.4.1e   4.   Identify the preposition in each sentence.

      Luke played games on his tablet.

      Marcy wrote a story about her vacation.

L.4.4b 5. Make nouns by adding the suffix -*ion* to these verbs.

select _____

inject _____

L.4.1a 6. Choose the correct relative pronoun. The antecedent can be a noun or pronoun.

Choose the sweater _____ you like best.

whom   who   that

L.4.1f 7. Fix this run-on by rewriting it as two or three complete sentences.

Daris is going to do a piano solo at our spring concert Phillip and Keith will play the trumpet the rest of us will sing.

_____

_____

_____

L.4.3c 8. Write F for formal English or I for informal English.

_____ You should totally read this awesome book!

_____ Please choose a book from the list.

L.4.1d 9. Underline the adjectives that tell shape, and circle the adjectives that state an opinion.

Amanda opened the beautiful square box.

Nicole had selected a delicate oval frame just for Amanda.

RF.4.3a 10. Choose the best word to complete the sentence.

I hope you are _____ for my birthday party.

available   explosion   reasonable

Lesson #98

W.4.5　1. Rewrite the sentence correctly.

Both Oprah Winfrey and Bessie Coleman described their
Childhoods difficult.
　　　　　∧ as

_____

_____

L.4.1c　2. Write a sentence using the verb *will* and a main verb that expresses an action that is going to happen.

_____

L.4.4c　3. Would you describe yourself as *audacious* or as *timorous*? Pick the word that you think may describe you. Then find that word in a dictionary or thesaurus. Write the meaning of the word you chose.

audacious　　_____

timorous　　_____

L.4.3a　4. A word's meaning changes with the emotions that are tied to it. In this sentence, what does the underlined word mean?

Wade's <u>mouth</u> gets him into a lot of trouble.

an opening　　　　a way of speaking　　　　a crime

L.4.1b　5. Complete the sentence. Choose the future progressive form of the verb.

Jenna _____ in the 5K
next month.

runs　　　will be running　　　is running

L.4.5b   6. Which adage fits the sentences below?

Yesterday, I forgot my lunch money, and Joan shared her lunch with me. When Joan's cat ran away, I helped her put up signs and look around the neighborhood.

_____ When the cat's away, the mice will play.

_____ There's more than one way to skin a cat.

_____ One good turn deserves another.

L.4.2c   7. Decide which of these is a compound sentence. Insert a comma.

_____ Tomorrow is Laura's birthday and I forgot to send her a card.

_____ I'll pick up a balloon and deliver it in person.

L.4.1e   8. Underline the prepositions. Use the *Help Pages* to check your work.

| above | walks | below | several | inside |
| during | lightly | people | around | noisy |

L.4.1a   9. Choose the correct relative pronoun. The antecedent can be a noun or pronoun.

Is this the book _____ you said I should read?

     whose   that   who

L.4.1f   10. Choose the group of words that is a sentence.

_____ Missed the bus.

_____ Mom took us to school.

_____ Late for class.

Lesson #99

L.4.1g　1. Choose the correct word.

Does anyone know (wear / where) I can find clothes to (wear / where) in the winter?

I felt (weak / week) all last (weak / week). I feel better today.

L.4.1e　2. **A prepositional phrase is made up of a preposition followed by a noun or pronoun.** What is the preposition in each prepositional phrase?

Kayla ate popcorn during the movie. _____

She shared the popcorn with Devin. _____

L.4.5a　3. Underline the two things being compared in the metaphor. Then write what the metaphor means on the line below.

The snow was a white blanket on the lawn.

_____

L.4.1a　4. *That* refers to things but may refer to people. Underline the relative pronoun. Draw an arrow to the antecedent.

The pile of dirt that gets moved is near the fence.

L.4.3a　5. In which sentence does the underlined word mean "an enclosed area for animals"?

A) Pablo needs to clean that <u>pigpen</u> he uses for an office.

B) Did you remember to latch the gate on the <u>pigpen</u>?

L.4.4a　6. Read the sentence.

We have picnics on the <u>patio</u>.

Choose the word most like a *patio*.

basement　　　bedroom　　　kitchen　　　porch

RI.4.7 **7 – 9.** **A pie graph shows how something is divided into parts.** This graph shows how much of each nutrient is found in a walnut. Look at the graph and use it to answer these questions.

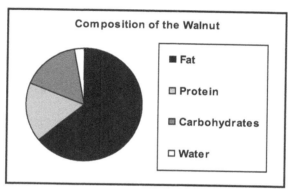

According to the pie graph, walnuts are mostly _____.

water   carbohydrates   fat

About what percentage of the walnut is water?

8%   63.8%   16.9%   16.5%

Which two nutrients are about equal
in the walnut?   _____

Where would you find a graph like this?

_____ A magazine article about the nutritional value of nuts

_____ A cookbook for special cupcakes

_____ An online website that sells baking supplies

L.4.4b **10.** Choose a word to complete the sentence.

The cotton shirt has been _____ so that it will not shrink in the wash.

precooked   preheated   preshrunk   preschool

Lesson #100

L.4.3a   1. A word can be positive or negative. Which word has the most positive meaning?

The outfit had a (babyish / immature / youthful) look to it.

L.4.3   2. Make a compound sentence from the two simple sentences.

Regina's father is a plumber. He fixed the leaky faucet.

_____

_____

L.4.3c   3. Write F for formal English or I for informal English.

_____ Watch out! That ice is super slippery.

_____ Please be careful not to fall on the ice.

L.4.2d   4. Write the plural of these words.

ox   _____

sheep   _____

duck   _____

fox   _____

L.3.1a   5. **Concrete nouns name things that can be experienced through the five senses. They can be singular or plural, common or proper.**

Underline the concrete nouns in each sentence.

Open your book to the glossary.

Use your scissors to curl the ribbon.

L.4.1b   6. Underline the verb that shows action that is in the progressive tense. Tell whether it is in the past, present, or future.

I was swimming at the pool yesterday.

      past   present   future

L.4.2a   7. Rewrite any capitalization errors on the line.

our class is reading "the celebrated jumping frog of Calaveras county" this june.

_____

L.4.2c   8. Add a comma in the following sentence.

Did you fall when you were hiking or did you cut your knee on a branch?

L.4.4c   9. Which word means "something that happened before a certain time"?
   A) postdate
   B) predate
   C) validate
   D) dateline

RI.4.5   10. **Cause** tells *why*; *effect* tells *what*.
   Is the underlined part of the sentence a *cause* or *effect*?

The temperature was 92°, so Ethan was very uncomfortable.

_____

Lesson #101

L.4.1e   1. Look at the prepositional phrase that is underlined. Find the preposition and write it on the line.

We looked for footprints <u>along the path</u>.   _____

L.4.5b   2. Read the sentence.

Sam says your problem is that you worry too much; I think he <u>hit the nail on the head</u> this time.

What is the meaning of the idiom?
A) Sam is good with a hammer and nails.
B) What Sam said was right.
C) Sam thinks people shouldn't worry.

L.3.1a   3. Underline the concrete noun(s) and circle the abstract noun in each sentence.

It is my dream to go to the Olympics.

Rick needs courage to hike in the woods without a flashlight.

L.4.1a   4. Underline the relative pronoun. *Who*, *whose*, and *whom* refer to people. Draw an arrow to the antecedent.

The people whose seats are at the top get the best view.

L.4.1f   5. Draw a line through the fragment.

We had all the ingredients we needed. Flour, sugar, butter, eggs. Now we had to mix the batter.

Rewrite the fragment as a complete thought.

_____

L.3.1a   6. Write past, present, or future to tell about the verb in this sentence.

I will walk to school with Lisa and Susan.   _____

L.4.1c 7. **The helping verb *can* works with a main verb in the present tense to show ability or to ask for something.**

Examples: ability: Senator Gray *can* speak at the rally.

asking: *Can* he have the stage at noon?

Underline the verb phrase in each sentence.

Jana can speak three languages.

Can Francis play the harmonica?

RI.4.5 8. Here is a set of directions for feeding a dog.
See if you can put the steps in the proper order.
Number the steps from 1 – 5.

_____ Next, get the gravy from the refrigerator and shake it well.

_____ Finally, put Fido's dish on the floor and call him, so he will eat.

_____ Then, measure two tablespoons of gravy, and stir it into the dog food.

_____ Put two heaping scoops of dog food into the dish.

_____ First, get Fido's dish and food out of the cupboard.

L.4.4a 9. Read the sentence.

Denzel loves to travel up the river in a <u>kayak</u>.

A *kayak* is a type of _____.

bicycle   car   train   canoe

L.4.1d 10. Underline the adjectives that tell color.

The acrobats bounded from violet cubes to magenta cylinders while juggling pink spheres.

Lesson #102

L.4.5c   1. Choose a synonym for the underlined word.

The tent was an acceptable <u>makeshift</u> home for the weary campers.

temporary   suitable   unacceptable   permanent

L.4.3a   2. Choose the word that has the most favorable or positive meaning.

Dacia just wants to (loaf / relax) all day.

L.4.1a   3. *That* refers to things, but may refer to people. Underline the relative pronoun. Draw an arrow to the antecedent.

Peacock blue is the paint color that I chose.

L.4.5b   4. Read the sentence.

"Don't even think about remedying the situation. It is <u>water over the dam</u> as far as I'm concerned," my neighbor assured me.

Which idiom matches the underlined idiom above?
A) Let bygones be bygones.
B) It's water under the bridge.
C) both A and B
D) neither A nor B

L.4.1b   5. Complete the sentence. Choose the present progressive form of the verb.

My team _____ the Giants at the park.

plays   will be playing   is playing

RI.4.5   6. Read the sentence.

Alexis was growing fast, so <u>she needed new shoes every few months</u>.

What does the underlined part of the sentence tell?

cause   effect

L.4.1e   7. Find and underline two prepositions in this sentence.

Thomas hid behind the oak tree and Maddie hid under the picnic table.

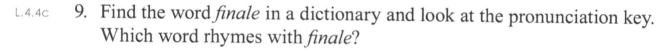

L.4.3   8. Draw a line between the subject and predicate in the following sentence.

Mrs. Jennings gives lessons on the clarinet, the drums, and the flute.

L.4.4c   9. Find the word *finale* in a dictionary and look at the pronunciation key. Which word rhymes with *finale*?

sale   spinal   trolley

What is the meaning of finale?

middle   beginning   ending   program

L.4.2b   10. Add commas and quotation marks.

Ms. Kane asked the class Who can find the area of this rectangle?

Multiply the length times the width replied Connie.

Lesson #103

RI.4.5   1. Read the sentence.

Joseph was an excellent pianist because <u>he practiced the piano exercises every day</u>.

What does the underlined part of the sentence tell?

       cause   effect

L.4.2a   2. Rewrite any capitalization errors on the line.

the wind chill registered minus 22 degrees fahrenheit in white bear lake, minnesota but the actual temperature was 10° f.

_____

_____

L.4.1d   3. Complete the sentence by writing the adjectives in the correct order.

> gold   stunning

A _____ _____ ring is in the jewelry store window.

L.3.1a   4. Underline all the adjectives in this sentence.

I dressed up my furry dog as a circus clown for the Halloween parade.

L.4.5a   5. Underline the two things being compared in the metaphor. Then write what the metaphor means on the line below.

My legs were jelly as I looked out from the stage at the audience.

_____

L.4.2c   6. Add a comma in the following sentence.

Van wanted to buy new tennis shoes but he didn't have enough money.

L.4.1f   7. The (subject / verb) is missing from this fragment. Correctly rewrite it as a complete sentence.

A big white tent in our front yard.

_____

_____

L.3.1a   8. Underline the verbs of being that show future tense.

The ducks will be in the water all afternoon.

L.4.1a   9. *That* refers to things, but may refer to people. Underline the relative pronoun. Draw an arrow to the antecedent.

We have many deer that live in

the neighborhood.

L.4.1e   10. Find the preposition in the prepositional phrase and write it on the line.

There is a shed <u>behind our house</u>.   _____

Lesson #104

RF.4.3a   1.   Choose the best word to complete the sentence.

I was happy to have the _____ of my warm coat and umbrella.

essential   additional   protection

L.4.1e   2.   Underline the prepositional phrase in this sentence.

Let's plant some colorful petunias and impatiens around the tree.

Write the preposition on the line.   _____

L.4.4a   3.   Read the sentence.

The clothing was <u>manufactured</u> in Taiwan but was <u>purchased</u> <u>elsewhere</u>.

Which of the underlined words means "in another place"?

manufactured   purchased   elsewhere

Which of the underlined words in item 3 refers to items that are made in a factory?

manufactured   purchased   elsewhere

L.4.1b   4.   Complete the sentence. Choose the past progressive form of the verb.

Our class _____ the new garden last week.

plants   was planting   is planting

L.4.3a   5.   Choose the adjective that has the most positive meaning.

Dani's brother seems so (intelligent / able / boring).

L.3.1a   6.   Underline the adverb that tells *where*.

Let's go downtown for the holiday parade!

L.4.1c   7. **The helping verb *could* is the past tense of *can*. It is also used with a main verb to show a possibility or to ask permission.**

Examples:

past tense of *can*	I could read by the time I was in first grade.
possibility	The car could be out of gas.
question	Could I get a notebook at the rest stop?

Underline the verb phrase in each sentence.

Could you help me with my homework?

Your name could be called next.

I could see the mountaintop when I sat by the window.

L.4.4c   8. Read the sentences. Use a dictionary or thesaurus to find a word to replace each underlined word.

The Youth Symphony is led by a <u>renowned</u> conductor. The musicians have to <u>rehearse</u> for several hours every day.

renowned   _____

rehearse   _____

L.4.1a   9. Choose the correct relative pronoun.

These are the teachers _____ will be honored tonight.

     whom   who   whose

RI.4.5   10. Does the underlined part of the sentence tell a *cause* or an *effect*?

Boyd and Dacey were excited when <u>they received an invitation to the birthday party</u>!

     cause   effect

Lesson #105

L.4.2d   1. Add the suffix. Write the new word.

busy + est → _____

L.4.1f   2. Correctly rewrite this fragment as a sentence.

Looking in all the empty boxes.

_____

_____

L.4.5c   3. Choose an antonym for the underlined word.

Rachel thought the wildlife documentary was beautiful and <u>fascinating</u>.

_____ boring

_____ interesting

_____ news

_____ hungry

L.4.2b   4. Add commas and quotation marks.

Clare asked What runs but never walks?

Cora answered Why a river, of course.

RI.4.5   5. Which of these states a *cause*?

A) Tristan was having trouble seeing,

B) so he had his eyes examined.

L.4.2c　6. Place a comma in both compound sentences.

LeShawn recommended a great mystery book but it was checked out of the school library.

I called the public library and they are holding a copy for me.

L.4.5a　7. Underline the simile in the following sentence.

Kristen's whining was like fingernails on a chalkboard.

What is the meaning of the simile?

A)　Kristen has long fingernails.

B)　Kristen likes to write on the chalkboard.

C)　Kristen's whining is very annoying.

L.4.1e　8. Add prepositions to complete the sentence.

Trevor ran _____ the playground

and _____ the tunnel.

L.4.2b　9. Add commas and quotation marks.

Dean chuckled Why do bees have sticky hair?

Because they use honeycombs replied Scott.

L.4.3a　10. Choose the word that has the most positive meaning.

William is very (immature / childish / youthful).

Lesson #106

L.4.4c   1. Find the word *vouch* in a dictionary. Which two words mean almost the same as *vouch*?

confirm   ignore   assure   heal

Which word rhymes with vouch?

touch   grouch   torch

L.4.1e   2. Underline the prepositional phrase.

Let's sleep inside the tent!

RI.4.5   3. Which of these states an *effect*?

A) Tristan was happy and relieved

B) because he could see clearly.

L.4.1a   4. *Who*, *whose*, and *whom* refer to people. Underline the relative pronoun. Draw an arrow to the antecedent.

We are looking for someone who will drive us to town.

L.4.1d   5. Underline the adjectives that tell *number* and circle the adjectives that tell *shape*.

Timothy dropped the bag of groceries, and the twelve oval eggs broke.

Timothy beat the eggs into the mix and made four dozen round pancakes.

L.4.4b   6. What is the root of these words? _____

employer   unemployed   employee   employment

L.4.1b   7.   Complete the sentence.   Choose the future progressive form of the verb.

Ms. Webb _____ to our class about her trip.

    spoke   will be speaking   is speaking

L.4.5c   8.   Read the sentence.

The tailor was poor and worked long hours for a <u>meager</u> salary.

Choose another word for *meager*.

    plentiful   unfortunate   payment   small

L.4.5b   9.   Choose a word from the word box to complete each proverb.

eggs	gifts	words	worm	nose

The early bird gets the _____.

Don't put all your _____ in one basket.

Don't cut off your _____ to spite your face.

A picture is worth a thousand _____.

L.3.1a   10.   **An abstract noun names something you cannot see or touch.**

Choose the abstract noun in each sentence.

Many freedoms are guaranteed by the Bill of Rights.

Peter wondered if he had run out of time.

Lesson #107

L.4.2c   1.   Add a comma where necessary.

We are getting a new movie theater and a new grocery store.

A movie theater is a great addition but we already have enough grocery stores.

L.4.1a   2.   Choose the correct relative pronoun.

People _____ were never farmers now own alpacas, which look like llamas.

which   who   whose

L.4.5a   3.   Underline the simile in the following sentence.

Without his glasses, the professor was as blind as a bat.

What is the meaning of the simile?

A)   The bat wears glasses.

B)   The professor had poor eyesight.

C)   The professor lost his glasses.

L.4.3a   4.   Choose the word that has the most positive connotation.

I like the (odor / scent / smell) of Edna's perfume.

L.4.1c   5.   Choose *possibility* or *past tense* to tell how the helping verb is used.

Last year, he could ride his bike to school every day.

_____ possibility

_____ past tense

W.4.5   6. Use the proofreader's symbols for "check spelling" and "take something out" to fix this sentence.

My grandmother she was cooking a turkey when suddenly the electrisity went out.

RI.4.5   7. Underline the *cause* in this statement.

There was a cold advisory, so school was cancelled today.

L.3.1a   8. **An abstract noun names something you cannot hear, taste, or smell.**

Identify the abstract noun in each sentence.

Brian expressed his creativity by writing music.

Her embarrassment was caused by her ripped coat.

L.4.1e   9. Underline the prepositional phrase.

Fluffy buried her bone under the bushes.

L.4.1f   10. Rewrite this run-on.

My friends came to my sleepover but we didn't sleep instead we watched movies, played video games, ate lots of snacks and talked and laughed all night long.

_____

_____

_____

_____

Lesson #108

L.4.1d   1. Underline the adjectives that tell size, and circle the adjectives that tell color.

An enormous brown moose lumbered out of the woods.

A tiny gray squirrel gathered acorns for the winter to come.

L.4.3a   2. Choose the most precise adjective.

The (smell / stench / aroma) from the skunk made my eyes water.

L.4.3   3. Circle each complete thought in this compound sentence.

It is early in the morning, but I am already tired!

L.4.3c   4. Write F for formal English or I for informal English.

_____ We had a crazy time yesterday!

_____ I am sure you will enjoy this.

RI.4.5   5. Underline the cause.

The floor was so slippery Nina dropped the computer.

L.4.4a   6. Read the sentence.

Earthquakes are unpredictable. No one can <u>foresee</u> when or where they will happen.

What is the meaning of the underlined word?

A) to be able to see a long distance

B) someone who studies earthquakes

C) to know about a thing before it happens

D) all of these

L.4.1e   7. Underline the prepositional phrase.

We love to hear music throughout the house.

L.4.4c   8. Read the sentences and look at the adjectives that are underlined.

At the Natural History Museum we saw <u>old</u> animals. Actually, they were the skeletons of <u>big</u> dinosaurs. The dinosaur called Tyrannosaurus Rex was a <u>scary</u> monster! We had a <u>good</u> time learning facts, and we took lots of <u>nice</u> pictures.

Use a thesaurus to write synonyms to replace each of the adjectives.

old   _____

big   _____

scary   _____

good   _____

nice   _____

L.3.1a   9. Underline the adverb that tells *where*.

Danny looked everywhere for his camera.

L.4.1b   10. Complete the sentence. Write the past progressive form of the verb *play*.

Jeremy _____ his guitar last night.

Lesson #109

L.4.1e   1. **A prepositional phrase begins with a preposition and ends with a noun (or pronoun).** Underline the prepositional phrase.

Marnie was amazed when she first looked through a telescope.

L.4.5b   2. Match each idiom with its meaning.

_____ see eye to eye   A) free of responsibility

_____ down to earth   B) agree

_____ footloose and fancy free   C) practical

L.4.1b   3. Complete the sentence. Write the past progressive form of the verb *collect*.

Michael and Emily _____ aluminum cans for recycling.

L.4.4a   4. Read the sentence.

The bicycle chain is <u>irremovable</u>.

What does the underlined word mean?
A) not repairable
B) not redeemable
C) not removable
D) all of these

L.4.4c   5. Find the meaning and pronunciation of the word *bough* in a dictionary. What is the meaning of *bough*?

tree branch   weapon

front of a boat   past tense of buy

Which word rhymes with *bough*?

buff   now   cough   none of these

W.4.5   6. This is the proofreader's symbol that tells you to make a letter lower case (╱). Draw this mark through the letter that should not be capitalized.

The Girls placed their car on the ramp.

L.4.3a   7. Choose the word with the best meaning for this sentence.

Nila likes her chili very (spicy / burning / warm).

L.4.5c   8. Choose a synonym for the underlined word.

The captain <u>piloted</u> the boat into the harbor.

     steered   flew   ignored   pushed

L.4.2c   9. Decide which of these is a compound sentence. Insert a comma.

There is a new superhero movie and we are going to see it tonight.

It isn't about Superman or Batman.

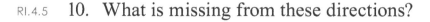

RI.4.5   10. What is missing from these directions?

Get some milk out of the refrigerator and fill a glass almost full. Be sure to put the container of milk back in the refrigerator. Next, get the chocolate syrup and shake it well. Then, pour the syrup into the glass of milk. Stir it with a spoon until the syrup is dissolved. Enjoy your chocolate milk!

A) The directions do not tell how long to stir the milk.

B) The directions do not tell how much syrup to add to the milk.

C) The directions do not tell how much milk to use.

D) Nothing is missing from the directions.

Lesson #110

L.4.1f 1. Draw a line through the fragment.

I could not wait for my cousins to get here. John and Karen. I always have so much fun when they come for a visit.

Rewrite the fragment as a complete thought.

_____

_____

L.4.1a 2. *That* refers to things but may refer to people. Underline the relative pronoun. Draw an arrow to the antecedent.

I saw the huge wave that knocked him over!

L.4.1d 3. Underline the adjectives that tell age, and circle the adjectives that tell color.

Ricardo bought a new green tractor, and now his old brown horse can graze in the pasture all day.

An ancient reddish plow sits abandoned nearby.

L.4.4b 4. The prefix *fore-* means "before or earlier."

The typewriter was a <u>forerunner</u> of the modern word processor.

What is the meaning of the underlined word?

_____ something that came after

_____ something that is used for writing

_____ something that came before

_____ someone who runs four laps

L.4.1e 5. Underline the prepositional phrase.

There may be skunks living under our porch.

L.4.3c   6. Write F for formal English or I for informal English.

_____ That's a wild snow fort!

_____ The snowflakes look beautiful.

centrosome

nucleus

nuclear
membrane

cell
wall

nucleolus

chromosomes   cytoplasm

RI.4.7   7 – 8. Look at this diagram of a cell.
                   Use the diagram to answer questions.

What is the cell mostly made of?

A) nucleus   C) cytoplasm
B) chromosomes   D) none of these

What is the nucleus enclosed in?

nuclear membrane   centrosome   cell wall

Where would you most likely find this diagram?

A) A science textbook in a chapter about cells

B) A magazine article about cell phones

C) A biography about the inventor of the microscope

L.4.1c   9. Underline the verb phrase in each sentence.

I may study piano next year. I might get a piano for my birthday!

L.4.4a   10.   Match each of the underlined words with its meaning.

                                A   B   C
The shipbuilders construct vessels that are seaworthy.

large watercraft   _____

build   _____

able to sail safely   _____

Lesson #111

L.4.5c   1.   Choose an antonym for the underlined word.

The first part of the movie was funny, but the <u>conclusion</u> was serious.

   ending   discussion   beginning   soundtrack

L.4.1g   2.   Choose the correct word.

I hope the doctor (knows / nose) why my (knows / nose) has been running.

L.4.1e   3.   **The words *between* and *among* are prepositions. Use *between* when speaking or writing about two nouns. Use *among* when speaking or writing about more than two.**

     Example: The captain had to choose <u>between</u> Ethan and Jacob.

Choose the best word to complete this sentence.

I had a choice (between / among) a movie and roller skating.

L.4.5a   4.   Underline the simile in the following sentence.

The night sky was black like coal.

What is the meaning of the simile?

A)   The sky was dark black.

B)   A moon was shining.

C)   Stars were out.

L.4.4c   5.   Look in a dictionary or thesaurus and find a better word to replace the underlined word.

Charles Brush became rich and was very <u>kind</u> to people in need.   _____

RF.4.3a   6. Choose the best word to complete the sentence.

The _____ could be heard from miles away.

A) available

B) explosion

C) reasonable

L.4.2a   7. Which of these should begin with a capital letter?

A) the pronoun I

B) the names of rivers, deserts, and forests

C) abbreviations that come from proper nouns

D) all of these

L.4.2b   8. Add a comma and quotation marks.

Anthony inquired When are we baking cookies with Grandma?

L.4.1b   9. Complete the sentence. Choose the present progressive form of the verb.

The doctor _____ the patient.

will be examining   is examining   examines

L.4.3a   10. Choose the word with the most positive meaning.

Aimee's puppy is very (scrawny / skinny / tiny).

Lesson #112

L.4.1d   1. Complete the sentence by writing the adjectives in the correct order.

bright   white

The cars shone under the _____ _____ lights
of the parking lot.

L.4.2c   2. Decide which of these is a compound sentence. Insert
a comma.

Do you want pepperoni or sausage on your pizza?

Harry is treating us to the pizza and Randy is
bringing a salad.

L.4.1f   3. What is missing from this fragment?   subject   verb

Going to Grandma's for dinner.

Correctly rewrite it as a complete sentence.

_____

L.4.2d   4. Write the plural of *country*.   _____

L.4.3   5. Name the sentence type.

Wipe your feet when you come into the house.   _____

RI.4.5   6. Remember, a *cause* tells *what happened*; an *effect* tells *why*.
Make up an *effect* to go with the *cause* below.

Cause: The hurricane was severe and lasted for three days.

Effect: _____

L.4.1a   7.   Choose the correct relative pronoun.

All of the items _____ you want are in this store.

whom   that   whose

L.4.1e   8.   Should you use the preposition *between* or *among*? Use *between* when speaking or writing about just two items. Use *among* when speaking or writing about more than two.

Examples: Paul had to choose <u>between</u> a skating party and a sleepover.

Helen had to choose <u>among</u> lemon, strawberry, and butterscotch.

Choose the correct preposition.

I chose (between / among) Hector, Louis, and Orlando for team captain.

L.4.4a   9.   Read the sentence.

It is <u>doubtful</u> that you will pass the test if you do not study.

What does *doubtful* mean?

certain   positive   pleased   unsure

L.4.5b   10.   Read the paragraph.

"I need to earn some money," said Shaun. "Should I ask Mr. White for a job?"

"Well, nothing ventured, nothing gained," said Grandma.

What does this saying advise?

A) It is better not to ask for too much.

B) It is better not to disturb people.

C) If you don't try, you will not succeed.

D) both A and B

Lesson #113

L.4.3   1. Underline the simple subject of this sentence.

Brush's invention allowed people to go out at night on lighted city streets and sidewalks.

L.4.3a   2. What is the meaning of the underlined word?

Use laundry bleach to remove <u>stubborn</u> stains.

_____ pig-headed

_____ willful

_____ hard to get out

L.4.1b   3. Complete the sentence. Choose the past progressive form of the verb.

Shiloh _____ all night long.

A) was barking

B) is barking

C) barked

L.4.5a   4. Underline the two things being compared in the metaphor. Then write what the metaphor means on the line below.

Our hands and feet were ice cubes after standing in the cold.

_____

L.4.2b   5. Add a comma and quotation marks to each sentence.

I can pass up any treats except Aunt Rose's cannoli admitted Donna.

I did not peek at my birthday gifts denied Bonnie.

L.4.1g   6. Write the correct word to complete the sentence.

brake   break

Only the front _____ worked when I tried to stop my bike.

The teacher promised us a _____ after we finished the test.

L.4.1c   7. Underline the verb phrase in each sentence.

If possible, I would like to be on the road by 9:00 a.m.

In the mornings, we would walk along the beach.

Would anyone like a glass of lemonade?

L.4.4a   8. Read the sentence.

A desert is a place where water is <u>scarce</u>.

What does *scarce* mean?

dry   plentiful   limited   hot

L.4.1e   9. **You can remember that *between* is used for two items this way. Between has a *tw* just like the word *two*. Use *among* for more than two.** Choose the correct preposition.

We divided the work (between / among) the two of us.

We shared the fudge (between / among) the three of us.

L.4.4c   10. Find the word *ruse* in a dictionary. What rhymes with *ruse*?

rush   lose   bus   none of these

Write another word that means the same or almost the same as *ruse*.   _____

Lesson #114

L.4.2a   1. **When you write the title of a movie, capitalize the first, last, and most important words in the title.**

Write the movie title correctly.

I heard the movie *bridge to terabithia* was based on an excellent book.

_____

L.4.1e   2. Choose the best word to complete the sentence.

You can choose (between / among) these three books for your book report.

L.4.3c   3. Write F for formal English or I for informal English.

_____ I feel kinda sleepy.

_____ One should get eight hours of sleep.

_____ Yikes, we're super late!

_____ You must be on time.

W.4.5   4. What does the proofreader's symbol tell you to do?

Most of the apples ⟨where⟩ green.   *sp*

_____

L.4.1a   5. Choose the correct relative pronoun. The antecedent can be a noun or pronoun.

I'd love to be the one _____ explores the unknown jungles.

that   which   who

L.4.2c   6. Add a comma in the following sentences.

A tornado roared through the neighboring town yet there was no damage.

Sometimes even a strong tornado does no damage nor does it cause any injuries.

L.4.2d   7. Add –*est* to form adjectives that compare.
        Example: long + est → longest

        loud →   _____

        wide →   _____

        cold →   _____

        cute →   _____

L.4.5c   8. Choose a synonym for the underlined word.

I tried to untie the tight knot, but my efforts proved <u>futile</u>.

easy   useless   successful   happy

L.4.1f   9. Correctly rewrite this fragment as a sentence.

Unwrapping the pretty packages.

_____

L.4.1d   10. Underline the adjective that tells age and circle the adjective that states an opinion.

Mama's sweet elderly neighbor is joining our family for Thanksgiving dinner.

Her energetic young granddaughter is driving her to our home.

Lesson #115

L.4.5a   1. Underline the two things being compared in the metaphor. Then write
             what the metaphor means on the line below.

             Veronica was a rock when she stood up to the girls who were
             bullying her.

             _____

L.4.4c   2. Look in a thesaurus or dictionary to find a more interesting word to
             replace each word that is underlined. Write the words below.

             Last summer we grew <u>pretty</u> flowers and <u>tasty</u> vegetables in our
             garden. We learned how to till soil and plant seeds. It was a
             <u>big</u> job but we had fun.

             pretty   _____

             tasty   _____

             big   _____

L.4.5c   3. Read the sentence.

             Mom was <u>aghast</u> when she saw how messy my room was.

             Choose a synonym for the underlined word.

                 delighted   horrified   hungry   special

L.4.1c   4. Underline the verb phrase in each sentence.

             The city council must vote today.

             Each council member may speak for five minutes.

             Could the secretary take notes, please?

W.4.5   5. Write what each proofreader's symbol means.

     /   _____

     ⅌   _____

     ∧   _____

L.4.4b   6. Use the prefix *dis-* to write a word
     that is the opposite of the word *agree*.   _____

L.4.3a   7. Choose the word with the most favorable meaning.

     Mrs. Dowd's grandson is very (unruly / active / wild).

L.4.5b   8. Choose a word from the word box to complete each proverb.

tricks	cake	safe	iron	roses

     Strike while the _____ is hot.

     Better _____ than sorry.

     You can't teach an old dog new _____.

     You can't have your _____ and eat it, too.

     Select one of the above proverbs and explain its meaning in your own
     words.

     _____

L.4.1b   9. Complete the sentence. Choose the future progressive form of the verb.

     Erin and Nicole _____ to the music on their MP3
     players.

       will be listening   listen   are listening

L.4.1e   10. Which is the correct preposition?

     Decide (between / among) the three of you, who will go first.

Lesson #116

L.4.1e   1. Choose the best word to complete this sentence.

You can choose (between / among) strawberry, lemon, and watermelon.

L.4.2d   2. Add one of these suffixes to the root word *hope*. Spell the new word correctly.   _____

-ing   -ness   -est

W.4.5   3. Use two proofreader's symbols to correct this sentence.

skateboarding is a very popular sport in America

RF.4.3a   4. Choose the best word to complete the sentence.

The Red Cross has an _____ need for volunteers.

A) immediate

B) distinguish

C) perpendicular

L.4.1d   5. Underline the adjectives that tell number and circle the adjectives that state an opinion.

Please place a dozen crunchy baguettes in the basket in the window.

A customer bought eight tasty macaroons and four buttery croissants from the window already.

L.4.2b   6. Add a comma and quotation marks.

The old man grumbled Gas prices are way too high!

L.4.2c   7. Add a comma where necessary.

Sandy had a sleepover last night and we played video games and painted each other's nails.

Next week, I'm having a sleepover but I think we'll decorate cookies and listen to music.

L.4.4a   8. Read the sentence.

My grandmother's <u>shears</u> are for cutting fabric, so we shouldn't use them for cutting paper.

What are shears?
A) sewing
B) knives
C) scissors
D) needles

L.4.1f   9. Draw a line to show where one sentence should end and another should begin.

One of my favorite summer activities is to find a good book to read I like to sit in the hammock under the big shady oak tree in my back yard to read it.

L.4.1a   10. Choose the correct relative pronoun. The antecedent can be a noun or pronoun.

Tribes _____ move around are called nomads.

that   whose   whom

Lesson #117

L.4.1a   1. **Relative adverbs tell *where*, *when*, and *why*. They begin a group of words that tells more about a noun. The relative adverb *where* means "in which" or "at which" and refers to a place.**

These words describe *park*.
↓

Example: That is the park where I take the dogs hiking.

↑
relative adverb

Circle the relative adverb. Underline the words that describe *field*.

That is the field where we play softball.

L.4.3   2. Circle each complete thought in this compound sentence.

Did you forget to set your alarm, or did you want to sleep in?

L.4.4c   3. Find the word *gander* in the dictionary and write one of its meanings on the line.

_____

L.4.2a   4. Which of these should begin with a capital letter?

A) holidays

B) island names

C) brand names

D) all of these

L.4.1b   5. Complete the sentence. Write the past progressive form of the verb *skiing*.

Hallie and Claire _____ last Saturday.

RI.4.7   6 – 8. Study the chart and use it to answer the questions.

Endangered Species			
Animal	snow leopard	Atlantic salmon	rhinoceros
Habitat	mountains	oceans	open range
Location	Asia	Europe & North America	Africa & Asia
Group	mammal	fish	mammal

Which animal is <u>not</u> a mammal?   _____

Which animal does <u>not</u> live on land?   _____

Which animal can be found in Asia
but not in Africa?   _____

Where would you find a chart like this?

A) a nonfiction reading selection on endangered species

B) an internet site on fishing for salmon in the Atlantic

C) a how-to manual on digging wells in the desert

L.4.3a   9. Choose the word with the most positive meaning.

We were given a (skimpy / meager / light) lunch.

L.4.5b   10. Match each idiom with its meaning.

_____ in a jam   A) calm down

_____ cost an arm and a leg   B) having difficulties

_____ chill out   C) very expensive

Lesson #118

L.4.1d   1. Complete the sentence by writing the adjectives in the correct order.

enormous   orange

An _____ _____ dinosaur is being
inflated in front of the movie theater.

L.4.5a   2. Underline the simile in the following sentence.

The baby's skin was soft as a rose petal.

What is the meaning of the simile?

A) The baby had very soft skin.

B) A baby's skin is pink.

C) Roses are pink.

RI.4.5   3. An *effect* is what happened. The *cause* is why it happened.
            Example: It snowed all night, so schools are closed today.

What?   Schools are closed. (*effect*)

Why?   It snowed all night. (*cause*)

Underline the cause in this statement.

Since there was no school, we played in the snow all day.

L.4.1b   4. Complete the sentence. Write the past progressive form of the
            verb *watch*.

Julian _____ superhero films at the drive-in.

W.4.5   5. Use two proofreader's symbols to correct this sentence.

People of all ages practice for hours for on speshel ramps.

L.4.1e   6. Underline the prepositional phrase.

Adam left his bike outside the front door.

L.4.3c   7. Read each sentence. Write F for formal English. Write I for informal English.

_____   I am pleased to meet you, sir.

_____   Wow, that's a sweet ride!

_____   I think your car is beautiful.

_____   Any chance I could go for a ride?

L.4.5b   8. Match each idiom with its meaning.

_____   all thumbs   A) clumsy

_____   chew the fat   B) clearly understood

_____   clear as a bell   C) talk

L.4.1a   9. Underline the relative adverb.

I found the wallet where you left it.

L.4.1f   10. What is missing from this fragment?   subject   verb

The large ferocious lion.

Correctly rewrite it as a complete sentence.

_____

_____

_____

Lesson #119

L.4.3a   1.   Choose the word with the best meaning for this sentence.

Let's (run / scurry / scamper) around the track a few times.

L.4.1e   2.   Underline the prepositional phrase.

Sean left his math book on the bench.

L.4.4a   3.   Read the sentence.

When cars were invented, the horse-drawn carriage quickly became an <u>outmoded</u> form of transportation.

Choose the meaning of the underlined word.

out-of-date   moving   a vehicle   modern

L.4.1b   4.   Complete the sentence. Choose the present progressive form of the verb.

The engineer _____ a new product.

will be designing   designs   is designing

L.4.5c   5.   Next to each word below, write S if it is a synonym for *friend* or A if it is an antonym.

_____ buddy

_____ pal

_____ foe

_____ ally

_____ enemy

L.4.1a 6. **Relative adverbs tell *where*, *when*, and *why*. They begin a group of words that tells more about a noun. The relative adverb *when* means "in which" or "at which" and refers to a time.**

These words describe *time*.
↓

Example: Midnight is the time <u>when we turn the clocks back.</u>
↑
relative adverb

Circle the relative adverb. Underline the words that describe *time*.

The winter months are the time when we celebrate my favorite holidays.

W.4.5 7. **Always begin the names of the days of the week with a capital letter.**
Use the proofreader's symbol to make corrections in this sentence.

On wednesday we have pizza, and we have tuna on thursday.

L.4.2c 8. Add a comma in the following sentences.

My new book is very heavy but it is filled with great stories and poems.

It is a present from Aunt Cordelia so I know it will be great!

RI.4.5 9. Remember, the *effect* tells what happened and the *cause* tells why it happened. Underline the *effect*.

Marie Curie was very poor, so she had to work to pay for her education.

L.4.4c 10. Are you somewhat *agile* or somewhat *awkward*? Circle the word that you think describes you, and then find the word in a dictionary. Write the meaning of the word you chose.

agile   _____

awkward   _____

95

Lesson #120

L.4.1d   1. Complete the sentence by writing the adjectives in the correct order.

fluffiest   pink

The movie star floated down the red carpet in

the _____ _____ sweater I have ever seen.

RF.4.3a   2. Choose the best word to complete the sentence.

Our class is making _____ toward our recycling goal.

equipment   compliment   progress

RI.4.5   3. Look for these words in *cause-effect* statements: *so, therefore, because, as a result of, since,* and *when.* Write cause or effect to tell which part of the statement is underlined.

Marie felt hungry because
<u>she had skipped breakfast</u>.   _____

L.4.1g   4. Complete each sentence with the correct word.

peace   piece

I can't finish the model airplane unless I find
the missing _____.

Mom always found a way to
keep _____ in the family.

L.4.2a   5. Correctly rewrite any words that have capitalization errors.

the postal worker said to write u.s.a. on the bottom of the
postcards i am mailing home from mexico.

_____

L.4.1f   6.   Correctly rewrite this fragment as a sentence.

Packing for their vacation in Florida.

_____

_____

L.4.1d   7.   Complete the sentence by writing the adjectives in the correct order.

| gigantic   prehistoric |

Our natural history museum has assembled the fossil bones of

a _____ _____ stegosaurus.

L.4.5a   8.   Underline the two things being compared in the metaphor. Then write what the metaphor means on the line below.

Jeff is a volcano when he doesn't get his way.

_____

L.4.1e   9.   Underline the prepositional phrase in this sentence.

I practiced piano until the sun set.

Write the preposition.   _____

L.4.1b   10.   Complete the sentence. Write the present progressive form of the verb *show*.

Mr. Delrosa _____

_____ us how to build

a bird house.

Lesson #121

L.4.4a   1. Read the sentence.

The marching band <u>incorporated</u> the <u>quickstep</u> into its <u>routine</u>.

Look at the underlined words.
Which word means "fast footwork"?   _____

L.4.2d   2. These words have the VCCV pattern. Cross out the word that is spelled incorrectly.

       carrpet   winter   cellar

Write it correctly on the line. _____

L.4.5c   3. Choose an antonym for the underlined word.

Patty was sick all weekend, and she is still feeling a little <u>feeble</u>.

_____ fragile

_____ weak

_____ strong

_____ frail

L.4.4c   4. Find the word *salve* in the dictionary and look at its meaning and pronunciation. Which letter is silent in the word *salve*?

     A) l

     B) e

     C) both l and e

     D) no letters are silent

RI.4.5   5. Do the underlined words state a *cause* or an *effect*?

<u>No one was home</u>, so Una walked to her grandmother's house.

        cause   effect

L.4.1e　6.　Underline the prepositional phrase in this sentence.

My lunchbox was wedged between the stove and the refrigerator.

Write the preposition.　　　　　　＿＿＿＿＿＿＿＿＿

L.4.4b　7.　Use the prefix *re-* to make words that match the meanings below.

fill again　　＿＿＿＿＿＿＿＿＿＿＿

view again　　＿＿＿＿＿＿＿＿＿＿＿

pay again　　＿＿＿＿＿＿＿＿＿＿＿

L.4.3c　8.　Read each sentence. Write F for formal English. Write I for informal English.

＿＿＿＿＿　What a bummer! The game was rained out.

＿＿＿＿＿　If it rains today, we can go tomorrow.

L.4.3a　9.　Choose the word with the best meaning for this sentence.

Maybe you can go to the zoo with us. Why don't you (beg / ask / implore) your mother?

L.4.2c　10.　Add a comma where necessary.

Mitch scored three goals in the playoff game yet we did not win.

We must win the next game so our defense will have to play better.

Lesson #122

L.4.2b   1. Add a comma and quotation marks.

Our team is the winner of the volleyball
tournament exclaimed the coach.

L.4.5b   2. **An adage or proverb is a wise saying that most
people think is true.** Read the proverb.

Two wrongs don't make a right.

What does this proverb mean?

A) Get revenge if you've been wronged.

B) Do not try to get even, because it only makes things worse.

C) Do the same wrong to the person who wronged you.

W.4.5   3. Write this sentence correctly.

You must wear safety Equipment when you skateboarding.
                                                        are

_____

_____

L.4.1b   4. Complete the sentence. Write the present progressive form of the
verb *try*.

Our class _____ to win the first place trophy.

L.4.1g   5. Complete each sentence with the correct word.

by   buy

We do not have enough money to _____ both
video games.

The parade marched right _____ our front door.

L.4.1a

6. Relative adverbs tell *where, when,* and *why.* They begin a group of words that tells more about a noun. The relative adverb *why* means "for which" and always refers to a reason. Sometimes the reason is not stated.

These words describe *reason.*
↓

Example: We don't know the reason <u>why you can't go.</u>

↑
relative adverb

Circle the relative adverb. Underline the words that describe the reason.

I don't know the reason why Sheri will not come to the play.

L.4.3c

7. Write F for formal English or I for informal English.

_____ I kinda like that story.

_____ Would you like chocolate or vanilla?

L.4.1f

8. Choose the group of words that is a sentence.

All of you.   We are not finished.   The red mitten.

RI.4.5

9. Choose the most likely *effect* for this cause.

The temperature outside is below 30°. Therefore we will _____.
A) stay indoors for recess
B) eat our lunches
C) rake the leaves

L.4.1d

10. Underline the adjectives that tell shape, and circle the adjectives that tell size.

A blue jay repeatedly tapped at its reflection in the large rectangular window.

My mother placed small round stickers and bigger square stickers on the glass to mask its reflection.

Lesson #123

L.4.4c   1. Use a dictionary to determine which word below means "the primary root of a plant."

     taproot   uproot   arrowroot

RI.4.7   2 – 3. Bar graphs are used to show how something changes over time or to compare items. Study the bar graph and use it to answer these questions.

What is the title of the graph?

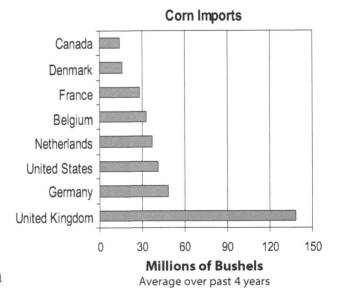

Corn Imports

Millions of Bushels
Average over past 4 years

_____

What amount of time is covered by the graph?

A) one year

B) ten years

C) four years

D) 150 years

According to the graph, Belgium imported about how much corn?

   30 bushels   a million bushels   30 million bushels

Where would you find a graph like this?

A) a news article comparing corn imports over the past 4 years in large and small countries

B) a magazine article about travel in the United States and Europe

C) a website devoted to uses for corn and corn products

L.4.1d   4. Underline the adjectives that tell number, and circle the adjectives that tell size.

We entered our two over-sized Great Danes in the dog costume contest.

They are sure to win in their tuxedos with six tiny bowties.

L.4.3   5. Circle each complete thought in this compound sentence.

The movie was great, but we ate too much popcorn!

W.4.5   6. Rewrite this sentence correctly.

We may have to eat sandwiches for
Thanksgiving dinner.

_____

_____

L.4.1e   7. Underline the prepositional phrase.

Rhonda stacked the boxes under the table.

Write the preposition.   _____

L.4.3a   8. Which word has the most negative meaning?

We saw the (slim / slender / scrawny) cat in the alley.

L.4.2c   9. Add a comma where necessary.

Marissa is traveling to New York and she is going to tour the
Statue of Liberty.

She wants to see the city from the Empire State Building so she is
hoping for a clear day.

L.4.5a   10. Underline the two things being compared in the metaphor. Then write
what the metaphor means on the line below.

Selma and her friends were worker bees decorating the gym
for the school carnival.

_____

Lesson #124

L.4.1b　1. Complete the sentence. Write the present progressive form of the verb.

We _____ at the beach watching the sunset.

　　sit　　　　　　are sitting　　　　were sitting

L.4.1f　2. Draw a line through the fragment.

The school carnival is one of my favorite events. Cake walk and cotton candy and obstacle course. I am going to go with my friends this year.

Rewrite the fragment as a complete thought.

_____

_____

L.4.4a　3. Read the sentence.

It is difficult to change the mind of an <u>obstinate</u> person.

Choose two meanings for *obstinate*.

　hard-headed　　mean　　easy-going　　stubborn

L.4.1a　4. Relative adverbs tell *where*, *when*, and *why*. Underline the relative adverb.

I want to work with animals when I grow up.

L.4.2b　5. Add a comma and quotation marks.

Marquis asked Why did the teacher wear sunglasses?

She had a very bright class giggled Alicia.

L.4.5b   6. Choose a word from the word box to complete each proverb.

Birds	A rolling	Pride	Measure	Curiosity

_____ stone gathers no moss.

_____ of a feather flock together.

_____ killed the cat.

_____ twice, cut once.

L.4.5c   7. Choose a synonym for the underlined word.

Laronda sang the lead in the musical's <u>finale</u>.
A) Mexican food
B) ending
C) beginning
D) songs

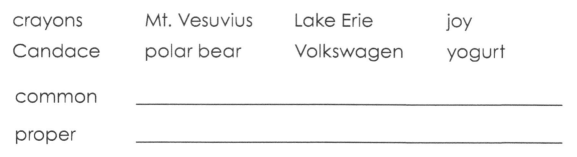

L.3.1a   8. Sort these nouns into two groups.

crayons   Mt. Vesuvius   Lake Erie   joy

Candace   polar bear   Volkswagen   yogurt

common   _____

proper   _____

L.4.1e   9. Find the preposition in the prepositional phrase and write it on the line.

The giant bullfrog perched <u>on the lilypad</u>.   _____

RI.4.5   10. Underline the *effect*.

The sidewalk is muddy because of storms and flooding.

Lesson #125

L.4.1e   1. Underline the prepositional phrase in this sentence.

It is muddy behind the garage.

Write the preposition.   _____

L.3.1a   2. Underline the object pronoun in the predicate of this sentence.

Grandma polishes it at least once a week.

L.4.4b   3. Match these prefixes with their meanings.

_____   *re-*   A) not

_____   *dis-*   B) again

_____   *pre-*   C) badly

_____   *mis-*   D) before

L.4.1f   4. Draw a line to show where one sentence should end and a new one should begin.

Every December my grandma bakes cookies with all her grandchildren I look forward to rolling the dough and cutting the cookies into different shapes and then decorating them with frosting.

L.4.2b   5. Add a comma and quotation marks.

Dakota boasted My grandma makes the best chocolate chip cookies.

W.4.5   6. **Always capitalize titles when they are used before a person's name**.

Example: a president   President Carter

Put the proofreader's symbol for capitalization under the words that should be capitalized.

We met governor Gilder and senator Shumaker!

L.4.1g   7. Choose the correct word from the word box to complete the sentence.

I'll	aisle	isle

_____ take this seat on the_____ as we cruise to the tropical _____ .

L.4.1a   8. Choose the correct relative pronoun. The antecedent can be a noun or pronoun.

Is that the kind _____ you like?

whom   that   whose

L.4.4c   9. Find the meaning and pronunciation of the word *sieve* in a dictionary. Which word rhymes with *sieve*?

give   heave   hive   leave

Choose two synonyms for *sieve*.

shirt   colander   blouse   strainer

L.4.3   10. Underline the complete subject.

The polka-dotted clown whistled a cheerful tune.

Lesson #126

L.4.2a   1. Rewrite the sentence correcting all capitalization errors.

The dallas public library has subscriptions to *national geographic world* and *time for kids*.

_____

_____

L.4.1b   2. Complete the sentence. Choose the future progressive form of the verb.

Krista _____ the cake for Dad's birthday.

baked   is baking   will be baking

RF.4.3a   3. Choose the best word to complete the sentence.

It was difficult to _____ the real diamond from the fake one.

A) immediate

B) distinguish

C) perpendicular

L.4.2b   4. Add a comma and quotation marks.

Mrs. Rodriguez explained If you turn your assignment in early, you will be able to enjoy your weekend.

L.4.1e   5. Choose the best word to complete the sentence.

Abigail had to choose (between / among) finishing her homework and practicing piano.

L.4.1a   6. Relative adverbs tell *where*, *when*, and *why*. Underline the relative adverb.

We played on the rock pile when we were small.

L.4.3 7. **When two sentences have the <u>same *subject*</u>, you can join them together to make one sentence with a <u>compound *predicate*</u>.**

   Example: Samantha raises chickens. Samantha sells their eggs.
               Samantha raises chickens and sells their eggs.

   The two sentences have been combined into one sentence with a compound predicate. Underline the compound predicate in the sentence below.

   Marie Curie grew up in Poland and studied in France.

W.4.5 8. Look at the proofreader's symbols and write the sentence correctly.

   <u>t</u>omorrow, Hannah and Jane∧drive to Freeport.
                                will

   _____

   _____

L.4.1f 9. Correctly rewrite this fragment as a sentence.

   Plates of roast beef, chicken, and turkey on the table.

   _____

   _____

L.3.1a 10. **An abstract noun names something that is thought or felt, like ideas or emotions.**

   Identify the abstract noun in each sentence.

   Paul hoped his luck would last until he arrived.

   The calico cat's curiosity often made him explore new places.

Lesson #127

L.4.1a   1. Underline the relative adverb.

She walks on the beach when the sun is rising.

L.4.1g   2. Match the correct spelling of each word with its definition.

_____ berry   A) (verb) to put or hide underground

_____ steel   B) (noun) a juicy fruit without a stone

_____ bury   C) (noun) strong hard metal made of iron and carbon

_____ steal   D) (verb) to wrongfully take another person's property or ideas

L.4.2a   3. Correctly rewrite any words that should be capitalized.

i heard karma barking and saw she had frightened ms. octave, my piano teacher.

_____

L.3.1a   4. Underline the past tense verb.

We filled the room with wreaths, balloons, and other decorations.

L.4.2b   5. Add commas and quotation marks.

Dale confided I'm glad we learned about standing up to bullies.

It gave me some ideas I can use on the playground Louie added.

L.4.4c   6. Use a dictionary or thesaurus to find the meaning of each underlined word.

Despite a change of habitat, coyotes manage to <u>subsist</u> throughout most of North America.

Ranchers are not fond of coyotes because they attack sheep and cattle, but some farmers may also have an <u>aversion</u> to coyotes.

_____

_____

L.4.4b   7. Use prefixes that mean "not" to write words with these meanings.

im-   "not proper"   _____

il-   "not legible"   _____

dis-   "not respectful"   _____

L.3.1a   8. Identify the abstract noun in each sentence.

The president spoke to the people about unity.

Courage did not come easily to the young man.

L.4.3   9. Combine these two sentences into one sentence with a compound predicate.

The tow truck hooked up the car. The tow truck towed it away.

_____

_____

L.4.1e   10. Underline the prepositional phrase.

Susan helped her friends before lunch.

Lesson #128

W.4.5   1. Write the sentence correctly.

(Tommorow) we're going to have the science fair.
        sp

_____

_____

L.3.1a   2. Underline two adverbs in this sentence.

You want to completely soak the sponge and wipe lightly.

L.4.3   3. These sentences have the same subject. Combine them to make one sentence with a compound predicate.

Marie was talented. Marie was hard-working.

_____

L.4.1e   4. Underline the prepositional phrase.

Drew hit the ball over the fence.

L.4.1a   5. Choose the correct relative pronoun.

Kate and Andrew are the ones
_____ are going to Ireland.

A) which

B) who

C) whom

L.4.1b   6. Complete the sentence. Write the future progressive form of the verb *move*.

My family _____ to Seattle in the summer.

L.4.2a　7. Place a check in front of the sentence that has correct capitalization. Correctly rewrite all words with capitalization errors on the line.

_____ claudia's favorite breakfast is Blueberry Pancakes at aunt emma's pancake restaurant.

_____ I asked Mom to buy Snickers, Skittles, and Kit Kats for Halloween.

_____ The return address was 866 stoney path, richfield, maryland.

_____

_____

RI.4.7　8 – 10. Study the graphs and use them to answer the next three questions.

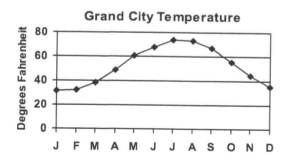
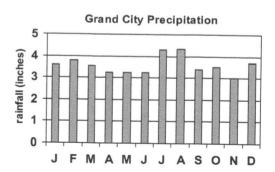

These graphs show:

A) temperatures in Grand City

B) precipitation in Grand City

C) both temperature and precipitation

What do the letters along the bottom of the graphs stand for? _____

July and August are the hottest months in Grand City. Which two months are the wettest?

_____

Lesson #129

L.4.2b   1. Add commas and quotation marks.

Alice questioned Why was the baby ant confused?

Janis giggled Because all of his uncles were ants!

L.4.1e   2. Underline the prepositional phrase.

Susan lives down the street.

L.4.1b   3. Complete the sentence. Write the past progressive form of the verb *smile*.

Grandma _____ when the whole family got together.

L.4.1g   4. Match the correct spelling of each word with its definition.

_____ role   A) (verb) turning over and over

_____ roll   B) (noun) the part someone plays

_____ wait   C) (verb) stay until something expected happens

_____ weight   D) (noun) the heaviness of a person or thing

RF.4.3a   5. Choose the best word to complete the sentence.

We were exhausted running through the _____ course.

percussion   obstacle   cooperate

L.4.4b   6. What is the root of these words?   _____

limitless   unlimited   limited   limiting

L.4.2a   7. Rewrite the sentence correcting all capitalization errors.

don't you think sinbad is a funny name for a french poodle?

_____

_____

L.3.1a   8. Underline all the adjectives in this sentence.

We spent the last hot, sunny day
swimming in the cold lake.

L.4.3   9. Underline the complete predicate.

Eva and Ron are getting on the subway.

L.4.2d   10. **When a word ends in a consonant + *y* pattern, usually change the *y* to *i* when adding a suffix.**

Add –*ly* and –*ness* to these words.

happy   _____

                 _____

sloppy   _____

                 _____

Lesson #130

L.4.1b   1. Complete the sentence. Choose the present progressive form of the verb.

Meredith _____ her story with the class.

     was sharing   shared   is sharing

L.4.3   2. Combine these two sentences to make a compound sentence. (Hint: use a coordinating conjunction.)

Neil Armstrong was commander of Apollo 11. Neil Armstrong was the first man to walk on the moon.

_____

_____

W.4.5   3. Look at the proofreader's symbols and write the sentence correctly.

we usually walk home insted of taking the trolley.
                             sp

_____

_____

L.4.4c   4. Use a dictionary or thesaurus to find the meaning of the underlined word.

Although the animal is known as a predator, hungry coyotes have been known to <u>plunder</u> watermelon crops.

_____

L.3.1a   5. Choose the correct pronoun.

The little dog brought a stick to Abby and (I / me).

RF.4.3a   6. Choose the best word to complete the sentence.

Make sure you observe the different _____ in the rock samples.

A) characteristics

B) discontinue

C) expensive

L.4.2d   7. Check the spelling of these plurals. Cross out any misspelled words.

sheep	boxs	trees
childs	wolves	clutches

Write the misspelled words correctly.

_____

L.4.1e   8. Underline the prepositional phrase.

Lizzie put the dishes in the cupboard.

L.4.1a   9. Underline the relative adverb.

I know the reason why you enjoy ice cream so much.

L.4.2a   10. Rewrite the sentence correcting all capitalization errors.

dad looks exactly like my grandpa who lives in scottsdale, arizona, and i look exactly like dad!

_____

_____

_____

Lesson #131

L.4.1f   1. Choose the group of words that is a sentence.

     _____ Every time it snows.

     _____ On time today.

     _____ It will never happen.

L.4.1b   2. Complete the sentence. Write the present progressive form of the verb *help*.

Our neighbors _____ to organize the block party.

L.4.1e   3. Underline the prepositional phrase in this sentence.

My bike fell off the rack.

Write the preposition.   _____

L.4.4b   4. The suffix *-less* means "without." Use the suffix *-less* to write words that match the meanings below.

without rest   _____

without a name   _____

L.4.1g   5. Choose the correct word from the word box to complete the sentence.

cent	sent	scent

My mom _____ me to the store to buy her favorite

_____, but I was more than one _____ short.

L.4.1a   6. Insert a relative adverb.

The old barn is the place _____ the baby calves were born yesterday.

L.4.3   7. Circle each complete thought in this compound sentence.

My dog can do tricks, and she is just plain adorable!

L.3.1a   8. Underline the concrete noun(s) and circle the abstract noun in each sentence.

The watchdog was fearless.

You can start a successful business with a good idea.

L.4.2b   9. Add commas and quotation marks.

The teacher asked her class What common 11-letter word is always spelled incorrectly?

The word is incorrectly shouted Billy.

W.4.5   10. Use the proofreader's symbols for "take out something" and "add something" to fix this sentence. Rewrite the sentence correctly.

It impolite to speak he when a player

is about to swing.

_____

_____

_____

Lesson #132

L.4.1g   1. Complete each sentence with the correct word.

deer   dear

The pearl necklace was very _____ to her.

The _____ disappeared into the dense forest.

L.4.2a   2. Which of these should begin with a capital letter?

A) automobile models

B) rivers

C) titles such as doctor or mister

D) all of these

RI.4.7   3 – 4. The line graph below shows changes over time. Use it to answer these questions.

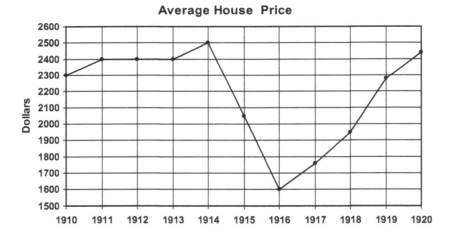

From 1911 to 1913 the average house price remained the same. What was it?   _____

In what year did the lowest average price occur?   _____

How much time is covered by this graph?

10 years   2 years   100 years   1 year

L.4.1b   5. Complete the sentence to show ongoing action in the future.

Andrew _____ quarterback for the team next year.

     is playing   will be playing   plays

RF.4.3a   6. Match the word with its meaning.

_____ fertile   A) worldwide

_____ global   B) first in rank

_____ primary   C) able to produce rich crops

L.4.3   7. Circle the subject of this sentence and underline the complete predicate.

They invited Charles to the year-end dance party.

W.4.5   8. Use the proofreader's symbols for "take out something" and "make lower case" to fix this sentence.

Carla rang the Bell, but no one was came to answer it.

L.3.1a   9 – 10. Underline the verb or verbs in each sentence and write them below.

Larry plays golf with Joel every day. Last year the boys learned the rules of golf. Now Larry and Joel swing the clubs pretty well. Larry lost the ball more times than Joel. Joel will work at the golf course next year. He will give lessons.

Past Tense Verbs   _____

Present Tense Verbs   _____

Future Tense Verbs   _____

Lesson #133

L.4.2a   1. Write the poem title correctly.

A crocodile tries to trick a dentist into examining his teeth in the funny poem "the dentist and the crocodile" by Roald Dahl.

_____

L.4.3   2. Underline the compound predicate in this sentence.

Emily entered the spelling bee and won second place.

L.4.1g   3. Choose the correct word.

I got the urge to (flee / flea) the moment I saw the first (flee / flea).

Felice won a giant panda when she (through / threw) the baseball (through / threw) the hoop five times in a row.

L.4.4c   4. Find the word *distance* in the dictionary. Write it in two syllables.

_____   _____

L.4.2b   5. Add correct punctuation.

How do you stop a bull from charging? pleaded Maggie.

Take away his credit card replied Maureen.

RF.4.3a 6. Match the word with its meaning.

_____ ignore   A) looking like a circle

_____ circular   B) pay no attention to

_____ pesticide   C) used to kill pests

L.4.4b 7. Look at these words.

preheat   prerecord   preshrunk

What does the prefix mean? _____

W.4.5 8. Use proofreader's symbols to fix two errors in this sentence.

Fern loved wilbur and wanted to save him

L.4.1e 9. Underline the prepositional phrase and write the preposition on the line.

Bison are giant shaggy animals that
once roamed across the Great Plains.   _____

L.4.1a 10. Insert a relative adverb.

The reason _____ we caught so many fish is we
knew the secret spot.

Lesson #134

L.4.1b   1. Complete the sentence. Choose the past progressive form of the verb.

David _____ to Mark on the phone last night.

A) talks

B) was talking

C) is talking

L.4.1f   2. What is missing from this fragment?   subject   verb

Ran in the big race yesterday.

Correctly rewrite it as a complete sentence.

_____

_____

L.3.1a   3. Underline the concrete noun(s) and circle the abstract noun in each sentence.

Her kindness made Rebecca pick her for a friend.

Riding the rollercoaster was one big thrill.

L.4.1e   4. Complete the prepositional phrase by writing a preposition on the line.

Kassie sat _____ her twin brothers.

L.4.2a   5. Correctly rewrite any words that should be capitalized.

i used legos to build a model of our house and used saran wrap for the smoky hill river.

_____

L.4.4b   **6.** What is the root of the words below? _____

perfectly   imperfect   perfection   imperfectly

L.4.2b   **7.** Add necessary punctuation.

What is black and white and red all over? asked Alex.

A penguin with a sunburn, of course answered Andrew.

RF.4.3a   **8.** Choose the best word to complete the sentence.

The company will _____ that product since no one uses it anymore.

A) characteristics

B) discontinue

C) expensive

L.3.1a   **9.** Choose the correct helping verb.

Jody's pet rabbit (had / have) run away.

L.4.1g   **10.** Complete each sentence with the correct word.

peer   pier

Several boats were tied up along the _____.

He leaned down to _____ under the bed but saw nothing.

Lesson #135

L.4.1g   1. Choose the correct word from the word box to complete the sentence.

| their | they're | there |

_____ is no way_____ going to drive all

the way to_____ grandmother's house before dark.

RF.4.3a 2. Choose the best word to complete the sentence.

We get more accomplished when
we _____ and work together.

A) percussion

B) obstacle

C) cooperate

L.4.1   3. The two sentences have been combined into one sentence with a
compound subject. Underline the compound subject in the sentence
below.

The classes and the principal went to the cafeteria for the
Kwanzaa festival.

L.4.2b   4. Add a comma and quotation marks.

Rudy asked Did everyone place his lunch order?

L.4.1b   5. Complete the sentence. Choose the future progressive form of the verb.

Nicole and Anthony _____ all the
decorations for the celebration.

A) made

B) will be making

C) are making

W.4.5   6. Use two proofreader's symbols to fix this sentence.

Kadira and i baked cookies on Sauturday.

L.4.1f   7. Correctly rewrite this fragment as a sentence.

Strong winds and heavy snowfall.

_____

L.4.2a   8. Rewrite the sentence correcting all capitalization errors

mrs. white watched jamal get on the plane to nevada.

_____

_____

_____

L.3.1a   9. Fill in a subject pronoun that agrees with the underlined words.

Addie and Mara live next door. _____ are sisters.

L.4.1e   10. Underline the prepositional phrase and write the preposition on the line.

The American bison image has
appeared on several U.S. coins.   _____

Lesson #136

L.4.1g   1. Choose the correct word.

It was a (waste / waist) of money buying these jeans because they are too big for my (waste / waist).

A police officer in (plain / plane) clothes boarded the (plain / plane) with the passengers.

RF.4.3a   2. Match the word with its meaning.

_____ orchestra   A) the one that came before

_____ population   B) the number of people living in an area

_____ previous   C) a group of musicians playing various instruments

L.4.2a   3. Place a check in front of the sentence that has correct capitalization. Correctly rewrite all words with capitalization errors on the line.

_____ In the battle of the colas at Highland School, Coke and Pepsi tied.

_____ i hoped grandpa could pick me up at the corner of parkview road and hillsdale avenue.

_____ Many people spend the day after thanksgiving shopping for christmas presents.

_____

_____

L.3.1a   4. Fill in the correct past tense form of the verb *grow*.

Akashi _____ beautiful flowers all summer.

L.4.4b   5. Write the meaning of each prefix.

       pre-   _____

       re-   _____

       mis-   _____

L.4.2b   6. Add commas and quotation marks.

       Jacob wondered What's the fastest way to get downtown?

       I would take the subway advised Amir.

L.4.1   7. These sentences have similar predicates. Combine them into one sentence with a compound subject.

       Halima is an excellent reader. Jelani is an excellent reader also.

       _____

       _____

L.4.1a   8. Underline the relative adverb.

       The bucket overflowed where the drain was leaking.

L.4.1e   9. Underline the prepositional phrase and write the preposition on the line.

       The bison ran toward the gate. _____

L.3.1a   10. Underline the adverb in each sentence. Draw an arrow to the verb it describes.

       Mrs. Young wrote clearly on the whiteboard.

       The students listened attentively to the speaker.

Lesson #137

L.4.2a
1. Which of these should begin with a capital letter?

    A) flavors of ice cream

    B) driving directions

    C) grandfather or uncle when written with a possessive pronoun

    D) none of these

L.4.1g
2. Complete each sentence with the correct word.

    won   one

    Sandra was the first _____ out of
    the starting gate.

    She would've _____ if she didn't
    trip on her shoelace.

L.3.1a
3. Underline the adverb. Draw an arrow to the verb it describes.

    The teens eagerly signed up for a chance to meet the rock star.

    We had to wait briefly before the movie started.

L.4.3
4. Draw a line between the subject and the complete predicate. Write
   S above the subject and P above the predicate.

    Sofia looked at the sparkling diamonds.

L.4.1e
5. Underline the prepositional phrase in this sentence.

    Livy wrote her name above the others.

    Write the preposition.   _____

L.4.1b   6. Complete the sentence. Choose the present progressive form of the verb.

Brian _____ his project at the science fair.

will be presenting   is presenting   presents

L.4.1f   7. Choose the group of words that is a sentence.

My dog chases cars.

The pink yo-yo.

Over and over again.

RI.4.7   8 – 10. Read the schedule for the Daily Rapid Transport and answer the
questions below.

Daily Rapid Transport --- Tremont to Treeville					
Bus Stop →		**Tremont**	**Campbell**	**Newberry**	**Portage**	**Treeville**
Bus Number	**1**	10:39	10:49	11:13	11:24	11:37
	2	---	10:55	11:19	11:30	11:44
	3	10:51	11:01	11:25	11:36	11:49
	4	---	11:31	11:42	11:56	12:11
	5	11:19	11:43	11:54	12:08	12:23

Can a passenger board the Transport in Campbell
after 10:30 a.m. and arrive in Portage by 11:30 a.m.?   _____

Mona boards the Transport in Newberry at 11:42 a.m.
What time does she arrive in Treeville?   _____

Derek lives in Tremont and takes flute lessons in
Portage. He needs to arrive in Portage by noon.
What is the latest time he can board the Transport in
Tremont and still arrive in Portage by noon?   _____

Lesson #138

L.4.4b   1. **The suffix -*er* can also mean "someone who does something."**
Example: A teacher is someone who teaches.

Write the word that means "someone who paints."   _____

L.4.1g   2. Choose the correct word.

We are (knot / not) going to be able to take a cruise if the sailor cannot undo the (knot / not).

Do you know (witch / which) (witch / which) parked her broom next to the scarecrow?

L.4.1a   3. Choose the correct relative pronoun.

The floor _____ my brother sanded looks great.

     that   whom   who

L.4.2b   4. Add commas and quotation marks.

Joey inquired Will you share your candy bar?

Of course, I'd love to said Susan.

L.4.3   5. Combine these two sentences into one sentence with a compound predicate.

Sheila is on the ice skating team. Sheila practices every day.

_____

_____

_____

W.4.5   6. Use two proofreader's symbols to fix this sentence. Rewrite the sentence correctly.

Mr. Bedelia teaches computer skills and at the unaversity.

_____

_____

L.4.1e   7. Underline the prepositional phrase in this sentence.

We enjoyed sleeping under the stars.

Write the preposition.   _____

L.4.1b   8. Complete the sentence. Choose the past progressive form of the verb.

The temperature _____ after the sun went down.

was falling   fell   is falling

L.4.2a   9. Place a check in front of the sentence that has correct capitalization. Correctly rewrite all words with capitalization errors on the line.

_____ Our plane is scheduled to land in capetown on saturday, september 15th.

_____ Mom bought Dad a Dr. Martin Luther King biography for his birthday next March.

_____ did i tell you i am reading harry potter and the goblet of fire before i lend it to Cherie?

_____

_____

L.3.1a   10. Circle the adjectives that describe the underlined nouns.

The woman parked her rusty old <u>automobile</u> by the high cement <u>curb</u>.

Lesson #139

L.4.1a   1. Choose the correct relative pronoun.

My uncle, _____ lives in Chicago, is coming for a visit.

A) that

B) whom

C) who

L.4.3   2. Combine these two sentences into one sentence with a compound subject.

Mary baked cookies for the church picnic. Antoine baked cookies for the church picnic.

_____

_____

L.4.2b   3. Add commas and quotation marks.

What kinds of birds do you think we will see? Carol wondered.

Margaret commented If you go with us, you may see the Indigo Bunting.

L.4.4b   4. Use the suffix -ful to write a word that means "full of waste."   _____

L.4.1b   5. Complete the sentence. Write the past progressive form of the verb teach.

My dad _____ me how to play golf.

134

L.3.1a   6. Underline the adverb. Draw an arrow to the verb it describes.

Please come early so you don't miss anything.

The community gave generously to the food bank.

L.4.1e   7. Find the preposition in the prepositional phrase and write it on the line.

The Atlantic puffin is a bird that can
"fly" through the water, too.   _____

As they hunt for food, their webbed
feet help them steer to the shore.   _____

L.4.1g   8. Choose the correct word.

No one is (aloud / allowed) to talk when another student is
reading (aloud / allowed).

Let's (meet / meat) at the coffee shop after I get (meet / meat)
from the butcher for tonight's dinner.

L.4.2a   9. Write these names correctly.

dr. vincent   _____

mrs. wilder   _____

uncle bob   _____

L.3.1a   10. In this sentence the subject and verb do not agree. Cross out the
incorrect verb and write it correctly on the line.

Pearl take her dog for a walk every day.   _____

Lesson #140

L.4.1g   1. Choose the correct word.

We can (sea / see) way out over the (sea / see) from the old red lighthouse.

She has filled her (pale / pail) with (pale / pail) pink rose petals.

L.3.1a   2. Underline all the adjectives in this sentence.

Marty got a shiny new tricycle for his fourth birthday.

L.4.2b   3. Add commas and quotation marks.

Good morning greeted Miss Jacka.

It's Teacher Appreciation Day! burst out Susie.

L.4.4b   4. The word *mobile* means "movable."
What does *immobile* mean? _____

W.4.5   5. Use the proofreader's symbol for "check spelling" to mark two words that are misspelled.

Bradley had a speshel friend who got vary sick.

L.4.1a   6. Choose the correct relative pronoun.

The hat _____ you wore matched your scarf perfectly.

A) that

B) whom

C) who

L.4.3　　7. Circle each complete thought in this compound sentence.

You could write to Aunt Ginny, or you could send her an email.

RI.4.7　8 – 10. **Another type of graph is a pictograph or picture graph.** Below is a pictograph showing the number of doctors in each country of a make-believe continent. Study the graph and answer the questions.

Doctors on the Continent of Dribster	
Nomadia	✚✚✚✚✚
Manistan	✚✚✚✚
Karenia	✚✚✚
New Trimburg	✚✚
Orany	✚

✚ = 10 doctors

How many countries are represented on the graph? _____

Usually, countries with more wealth have more doctors and better medical care. Which country do you think is the wealthiest? _____

According to the graph, which statement is true?

A) Karenia has three doctors and a population of 1,000 people.

B) Karenia has thirty doctors.

C) Karenia has three doctors.

What information is <u>not</u> given in this graph?

_____ the title of the graph

_____ the population of each country

_____ the name of each country

_____ a key

Simple Solutions.
Minutes a Day—Mastery for a Lifetime!

Common Core
ENGLISH GRAMMAR
& Mechanics

4

Help Pages

Some material addressed in standards covered at earlier grade levels
may not be available in these *Help Pages*, but you can access all grade levels
of *Simple Solutions Common Core English Grammar & Mechanics Help Pages* at
SimpleSolutions.org.

Help Pages

Parts of Speech - Nouns

A **common noun** names a person, place, thing, or idea. A **proper noun** names a particular person, place, thing or idea. A proper noun begins with a capital letter. Nouns may be singular or plural.

Some of the Functions of Nouns

Subject	The subject is whom or what the sentence is about. *Example*: <u>Tom</u> likes to play piano.
Direct Object	A direct object receives the action of the verb. *Example*: Tom plays the <u>piano</u>. To find the DO, ask: Tom plays what?
Possessive	A possessive noun shows ownership and usually modifies another noun. *Examples*: <u>Mr. Gore's</u> class uses <u>Tom's</u> piano.

Parts of Speech - Pronouns

A **pronoun** takes the place of a noun. The noun that the pronoun is referring to is called the **antecedent**. The antecedent is in the same sentence or a recent, earlier sentence; occasionally, an antecedent is not specifically named. It is implied, or "understood."

Examples: The <u>puppy</u> is in <u>its</u> pen.
("<u>its</u> pen" refers to the puppy's pen, so "puppy" is the antecedent.)
<u>It</u> has been raining all day.
(There is no clear antecedent, but we know "it" refers to the weather.)

Personal Pronouns

Subject Pronouns	Used as the subject of a sentence or clause *Singular*: I, you, he/she, it *Plural*: we, you, they
Object Pronouns	Used as an object; found in the predicate of a sentence *Singular*: me, you, him/her, it *Plural*: us, you, them
Possessive Pronouns	Used to show ownership; modify nouns *Singular*: my, mine*, your, yours*, his*, her, hers*, its* *Plural*: our, ours*, your, yours*, their, theirs* * These can stand alone.
Relative Pronouns	Connect incomplete thoughts to complete thoughts (that, which, who, whom, whose, whoever, whomever, whichever, whatever) *Example*: She is the one <u>who</u> won the prize.

Parts of Speech - Conjunctions

Coordinating Conjunctions	Join two equal elements or two complete thoughts Use the acronym FANBOYS (for, and, nor, but, or, yet, so) to remember them. *Example*: We swam in the ocean <u>and</u> roasted hot dogs over the fire.

Help Pages

Parts of Speech - Adjectives

Adjectives modify nouns or pronouns. Adjectives tell *how many, what color, how big, how small, what kind*, and so on.   **Example**: He was a <u>tall</u> man.
A proper adjective begins with a capital letter.   **Example**: <u>Siberian</u> Husky
An **article** is a special type of adjective (a, an, the).   **Example**: Throw Jack <u>the</u> ball.

Conventional Adjective Patterns

There is an accepted pattern to the order of speaking or writing types of adjectives. This table shows types of adjectives and the order in which they would normally be spoken or written.

Number	Observation or opinion	Physical properties				Noun
		Size	Shape	Age	Color	
seven	beautiful	large			blue	marbles
dozen		small	oval			eggs
a	slow			old		turtle
couple	smart			young		toddlers

Parts of Speech - Verbs

Action   Shows an action
           Example: A stunt man <u>performs</u> dangerous feats.
                   The symphony <u>performs</u> every Sunday.

Being   Does not show action; shows a state of being
           Examples: is, are, was, were, be, am, being, been

Helping   Pairs with a main verb to form a verb phrase
           Examples: is, are, was, were, be, am, being, been, might, could, should, would, can, do, does, did, may, must, will, shall, have, has, had

Verb Tense

Verb tense tells the time when the action or condition of the verb occurs.

Simple Verb Tenses

Present   The action is occurring now or is unchanging.
                                    The house <u>is</u> new. (singular subject)
                                    The boys <u>swim</u>. (plural)

Past   The action was started and completed in the past.
                                    The clock <u>stopped</u>. (singular subject)
                                    The buses <u>ran</u>. (plural)

Future   The action will not start until the future.
                                    The snow <u>will fall</u>. (singular subject)
                                    The lakes <u>will freeze</u>. (plural)

Progressive Verb Tenses

A main verb that ends in *–ing* works with a helping verb to form the progressive tense.

Present   She <u>is sleeping</u>.   **Past**   She <u>was sleeping</u>.   **Future**   She <u>will be sleeping</u>.
           They <u>are eating</u>.   They <u>were eating</u>.   They <u>will be eating</u>.

Help Pages

Irregular Verbs

Present	Past	Use with *has, have,* or *had*		Present	Past	Use with *has, have,* or *had*
am/is/are	was/were	been		keep	kept	kept
begin	began	begun		make	made	made
blow	blew	blown		mistake	mistook	mistaken
break	broke	broken		ride	rode	ridden
bring	brought	brought		ring	rang	rung
build	built	built		say	said	said
choose	chose	chosen		shrink	shrank	shrunk
do	did	done		sing	sang	sung
draw	drew	drawn		speak	spoke	spoken
drink	drank	drunk		steal	stole	stolen
drive	drove	driven		stink	stank	stunk
eat	ate	eaten		swim	swam	swum
fall	fell	fallen		teach	taught	taught
fly	flew	flown		tear	tore	torn
freeze	froze	frozen		tell	told	told
get	got	gotten		think	thought	thought
grow	grew	grown		throw	threw	thrown
have	had	had		wear	wore	worn

Parts of Speech - Prepositions

Prepositions relate nouns or pronouns to other words in the sentence. A **prepositional phrase** begins with a preposition and ends with a noun or a pronoun.

Some Common Prepositions

about	around	by	into	out	under
above	before	down	near	outside	underneath
across	behind	during	nearby	over	until
after	below	except	next to	past	up
against	beneath	for	of	through	upon
along	beside	from	off	throughout	with
alongside	between	in	on	to	within
among	beyond	inside	onto	toward	without

Help Pages

Parts of Speech - Adverbs

Adverbs modify verbs, adjectives, or other adverbs.

Adverbs That Tell *When*

after	before	finally	never	often	until	while
always	earlier	later	next	sometimes	when	yesterday

Adverbs That Tell *How*

beautifully	eagerly	greedily	noisily	politely	quietly	selfishly
calmly	gracefully	loudly	perfectly	quickly	sadly	wildly

Adverbs That Tell *Where*

back	down	forward	in	outside	there	up
behind	everywhere	here	inside	somewhere	under	upward

Adverbs That Tell *To What Extent*

almost	completely	extremely	rather	scarcely	thoroughly	totally
also	entirely	quite	really	somewhat	too	very

Sentences

A **sentence** is a complete thought that includes a subject and a verb.

Features of a sentence:
1. begins with a capital letter
2. ends with punctuation/end mark
3. conveys a complete thought

Parts of a Sentence

Subject   The **simple subject** tells whom or what the sentence is about but does not include any words that describe the subject.

The **complete subject** includes the simple subject plus all of the modifiers that go with it.

Example: A few hungry **teenagers** devoured the pizza. *Teenagers* is the simple subject. *A few hungry teenagers* is the complete subject.

Predicate   The **simple predicate** is the verb.

The **complete predicate** is the verb plus the other words that say something about the subject – what the subject is or does.

Example: The tired children **climbed** slowly upstairs. *Climbed* is the simple predicate, or verb. *Climbed slowly upstairs* is the complete predicate.

The Four Sentence Types

Type	Other Name	Punctation	Example:
declarative	statement	period	This is a sentence.
interrogative	question	question mark	Is this correct?
imperative	command/request	period	Please open the door.
exclamatory	exclamation	exclamation point	This is awesome!

Help Pages

Sentences (continued)

Fragments

A fragment is not a sentence because it does not express a complete thought. A fragment is missing either a subject or a verb.

Examples: The book that I read. (missing a verb)

Running down the street. (missing a subject)

Run-on Sentences

A run-on is two or more complete thoughts that run together without proper punctuation or conjunctions.

Examples:

Incorrect: The twins really wanted to ride the rollercoaster there was a height requirement they were too short decided to ride the Ferris wheel instead.

Correct: The twins really wanted to ride the rollercoaster. There was a height requirement, and they were too short. They decided to ride the Ferris wheel instead.

Sentence Structure

Simple	**Parts**: subject and predicate only **Example**: We will hold a rally at the local park.
Compound	**Parts**: two or more complete thoughts **Joined by**: coordinating conjunction **Example**: There will be speeches in the morning, and we will play games in the afternoon.
Complex	**Parts**: one complete thought and one or more incomplete thoughts **Joined by**: subordinating conjunction **Example**: I took my umbrella because it was raining.

Punctuation

Commas (,)	Use commas to separate words or phrases in a series. ***Example***: Sun brought a coloring book, some crayons, and a pair of scissors.
	Use a comma to separate two independent clauses joined by a conjunction. ***Example***: Dad works in the city, and he is a commuter.
	Use a comma to separate two words or two numbers when writing a date. ***Example***: Friday, April 8, 2011
	Use a comma between the city and state in an address. ***Examples***: Boston, MA Seattle, WA Honolulu, HI
	Use commas in greetings and closings of letters. ***Examples***: Dear Mr. Clydesdale, Sincerely yours,
Apostrophe (')	Use an apostrophe to form a contraction or a possessive noun. ***Examples***: I don't want to go. That was Sherry's little sister.
End marks	Use end punctuation for sentences. *See* **Four Sentence Types**.

Help Pages

Punctuation (continued)
Commas and Quotation Marks in Dialogue
Put quotation marks before and after the actual words that someone says. Quotation marks are like a frame around spoken words. Keep the end mark inside the quotes. *Example*:   She said, "We need to go now."
Capitalize the first word of a sentence in quotes. *Example*: "Wait," said Sam, "the door is locked."
Use a comma or end mark before and after a quote. *Examples*: "It's starting to rain!" Marcy exclaimed.   Mickey replied, "Don't worry, you won't melt."
Do not use a comma at the end of a sentence within quotes if there is another end mark. *Example*:   "Grandma's here!" exclaimed Sasha.
Capitalization Rules
Capitalize the first word in a sentence, the pronoun *I*, proper nouns, and proper adjectives.
Capitalize names of days and months.
Capitalize holidays, product names, and geographic names. These are all proper nouns.
Capitalize the first, last and the important words in titles. *Example*:   *From the Mixed-Up Files of Mrs. Basil E. Frankweiler*
Other Types of Punctuation

Punctuating Titles
Show the title of a book, movie, play, television show, magazine, or website by using italics or by underlining it.
Examples: *Sarah, Plain and Tall*   or   <u>Sarah, Plain and Tall</u>
              Peter and the Wolf   or   <u>Peter and the Wolf</u>
              Sesame Street   or   <u>Sesame Street</u>
Put quotation marks around the title of a short work, such as a poem, song, short story, article or book chapter.
Examples: "Dreams" is a poem by Langston Hughes.
              We sang "Jingle Bells" and many other winter songs.
              "The Monkey's Paw" is a scary short story by W.W. Jacobs.
              In <u>My Side of the Mountain</u>, by Jean Craighead George, one of the chapters is called "The Old, Old Tree."

Help Pages

Proofreader's Symbols

Description	Symbol	Example
Make capital	≡	the car raced down the street.
Add something	∧	The car raced down street. the
Make lower case	/	The Car raced down the street.
Take something out	℘	The car raced down the the street.
Check spelling	⬭ sp	The cor raced down the street.
Indent	¶	The car raced down the street.
Add end punctuation	⊙ ! ?	The car raced down the street ⊙

Greek and Latin Roots and Affixes and Their Meanings

Word Part	Meaning	Word Part	Meaning
able, ible	able to	hema	blood
anti	against	il	opposite
auto	self	im/in	not
bio	life	ion, tion, sion	forms noun from verb
centi	hundred	ment	state of
co	together	mono	one
dec	ten	ology	study of
dent	tooth	port	carry
dia	across	pre	before
dis	not	re	again
er	one who does	scrip	to write
ess	female	sent	feel
ful	full of	ty, ity	forms noun from adjective
graph, gram	written	un	not

Help Pages

Figurative Language

A **simile** is a way to describe something using a comparison. A simile compares two things using the words *like* or *as*.

Example: The baby is *as playful as a kitten*. (A baby is compared to a kitten.)

A **metaphor** compares two things but does not use *like* or *as*. It uses a form of the verb *be*.

Example: Joey is *a magnet for bad luck*. (He attracts bad luck.)

An **idiom** is a phrase whose meaning can't be understood from the literal meaning of the words.

Example: *This article is way over my head*. (This phrase could mean something is taller than I am. But when *over my head* is an idiom, it means something is too complicated to be understood.)

Examples: We bought a used car, and it's <u>a real lemon</u>!
(refers to a car that has many problems or doesn't run)

At first I was angry, but I <u>got over it</u>.
(refers to letting go of something that was upsetting)

An **adage** or **proverb** is a wise saying that most people think is true. It may give advice.

Example: *All that glitters is not gold*. (This saying warns us that something might seem valuable, but really is not valuable.)

Spelling Rules

Adding Prefixes

When adding a prefix or joining two words, do not change the spelling of the base word.
Examples: pre<u>cook</u>, <u>cook</u>book

Adding Suffixes that Begin with a Consonant

When adding a suffix that begins with a consonant, do not change the spelling of the base word.

Examples:	joy + ful → joyful	wool + ly → woolly	agree + ment → agreement
	pain + ful → painful	sincere + ly → sincerely	govern + ment → government
Common Exceptions:	argue + ment → argument	true + ly → truly	nine + th → ninth
	judge + ment → judgment	due + ly → duly	awe + ful → awful

Adding Suffixes that Begin with a Vowel

When a word ends in a **vowel + y**, add a suffix without changing the spelling of the base word.

| *Examples*: | employ + er → employer | play + ing → playing |
| | gray + est → grayest | enjoy + ment → enjoyment |

When a word ends in **silent -e**, usually drop the -e to add a suffix that begins with a vowel.
Examples: love + able → lovable

Help Pages

Spelling Rules (continued)

Adding Suffixes that Begin with a Vowel

When a word ends in a **consonant + y** pattern, usually change the *y* to *i* when adding a suffix.

> ***Examples***: try + ed → tried   (ends in consonant + *y*; change the *y* to *i*)

Do not change the *y* to *i* if the word ends in a vowel + *y* pattern or if the suffix is *ing*.

> ***Examples***: destroy + ed → destroyed   (vowel + *y*)
>
> hurry + ing → hurrying   (suffix is ing)

When a one-syllable word ends in the **CVC pattern (consonant - vowel - consonant)**, usually double the final consonant to add a suffix that begins with a vowel.

> ***Examples***: ship + ing → shipping   (suffix begins with a vowel)
>
> ship + ment → shipment   (suffix begins with a consonant)
>
> nut + y → nutty   (suffix is *y*)

When a one-syllable word ends in the **CVC pattern**, and the final consonant is **s**, **x** or **w**, do not double the final consonant.

> ***Examples***: mix + ing → mixing   box + ed → boxed   slow + er → slower

When a multi-syllable word ends in the **CVC pattern**, and the **accent is on the last syllable**, usually double the final consonant to add a suffix that begins with a vowel.

> ***Example***:   commit + ing → committing   (suffix begins with a vowel)

Common Exception: prefer + able → preferable

Making Plurals

When a word **ends in s, x, z, ch, or sh** add -es to make the plural

> ***Examples***: tax → taxes; wish → wishes

Many words that **end in f or fe,** change the *f* or *fe* to -ves.

> ***Examples***: life → lives; thief → thieves

Other words that **end in f or ff** do not follow the rule for making plurals.

> ***Examples***: cliff → cliffs; belief → beliefs

Irregular plural nouns have a completely different spelling in the plural form.

Common irregular plural nouns							
child	children	man	men	ox	oxen	tooth	teeth
louse	lice	mouse	mice	person	people	woman	women

Additional Spelling Rule

Place *i* before *e*, except after *c*, or when sounded like /ā/ as in neighbor and weigh.

> ***Examples***: mischief   receive   eight

There are many exceptions to spelling rules. If you are not sure of the spelling of a word, use a dictionary to check.